Harold R Foster

MW00634014

Prince Valiant

COMPRISING PAGES 1051 THROUGH 1096

The Red Stallion

FANTAGRAPHICS BOOKS

ABOUT THIS EDITION:

Produced in cooperation with the Danish publisher Interpresse and several other publishers around the world, this new edition of PRINCE VALIANT is intended to be the definitive compilation of Hal Foster's masterpiece.

In addition to this volume, Fantagraphics has in stock twenty-one more collections of Foster's Prince Valiant work (Vols. 1, 5-23 and 26). The ultimate goal is to have the entirety of Hal Foster's epic, comprising 40 volumes, in print at once.

ABOUT THE PUBLISHER:

FANTAGRAPHICS BOOKS has dedicated itself to bringing readers the finest in comic book and comic strip material, both new and old. Its "classics" division includes *The Complete E.C. Segar Popeye*, the *Complete Little Nemo in Slumberland* hardcover collection, and *Pogo* and *Little Orphan Annie* reprints. Its "modern" division is responsible for such works as Yellow Kid Award-winner *Love and Rockets* by Los. Bros. Hernandez, Peter Bagge's *Hate*, Daniel Clowes's *Eightball*, and American editions of work by Muñoz & Sampayo, Alberto Breccia, and F. Solano Lopez, as well as *The Complete Crumb Comics*.

PREVIOUS VOLUMES IN THIS SERIES:

Volume 1: "The Prophecy"
Volume 2: "The Singing Sword" *(out of print)*
Volume 3: "Knights of the Round Table *(out of print)*
Volume 4: "The Menace of the Hun" *(out of print)*
Volume 5: "The Sea King"
Volume 6: "Journey to Africa"
Volume 7: "The Roman Wall"
Volume 8: "Prince of Thule"
Volume 9: "Journey to the Misty Isles"
Volume 10: "Aleta"
Volume 11: "Intrigues at Camelot"
Volume 12: "The New World"
Volume 13: "The Sun Goddess"
Volume 14: "Sword and Sorcery"
Volume 15: "Young Geoffrey"
Volume 16: "Love and War"
Volume 17: "Return from Rome"
Volume 18: "The Stolen River"
Volume 19: "Duel in Ireland"
Volume 20: "The Pilgrimage"
Volume 21: "Prisoner of the Khan"
Volume 22: "Homeward Bound"
Volume 23: "The Kings of Cornwall"
Volume 26: "Lithway's Law" *(out of print)*
Volume 27: "The Eternal Quest" *(out of print)*
Volume 28: "The Savage Girl" *(out of print)*
Volume 29: "Monastery of the Demons"
Volume 30: "Arn, Son of Valiant" *(out of print)*
Volume 31: "A Joust for Aleta" *(out of print)*

PRINCE VALIANT, Volume 24
"THE RED STALLION"
comprising pages 1051 (March 30, 1957) through 1096 (February 9, 1958)
Published by Fantagraphics Books, 7563 Lake City Way NE, Seattle, WA 98115
Editorial Co-Ordinator: Pia Christensen
Colored by Montse Serra of Bardon Art, S.A.
Cover inked by Mårdøn Smet and colored by Montse Serra
Fantagraphics Books staff: Kim & Mark Thompson

Printed in Denmark
ISBN 1-56097-167-3
First Printing: Spring, 1995

Prince Valiant
IN THE DAYS OF KING ARTHUR
BY HAROLD R FOSTER
Our Story: IT IS A GRIM AND HEARTSICK PRINCE VALIANT WHO WALKS SLOWLY TOWARD THE ENCAMPMENT; A MAN WITHOUT HONOR, FOR HE HAS SWORN FEALTY TO A KING HE IS DETERMINED TO DESTROY!

A SPRAWLING, DIRTY CAMP WHERE THIEVES AND RAIDERS, CUTTHROATS AND THE VICIOUS SCUM OF MANY NATIONS BRAWL AND CAROUSE.

DOWN BY THE SHIPS EACH BAND OF SEA RAIDERS JEALOUSLY GUARDS ITS LOOT AND PROVISIONS. FOR THE HOST IS COMPOSED OF MANY SMALL, INDEPENDENT GANGS WHO DISTRUST EACH OTHER, AND THERE IS NO ACKNOWLEDGED LEADER.

ONLY THE PROMISE OF PLUNDER HOLDS THIS MOB TOGETHER. FROM THE WATCHTOWER VAL STUDIES THE ARMY THAT IS SOON TO BE LOOSED ON BRITAIN, AND SLOWLY A PLAN FORMS.

AT THE WAR COUNCILS VAL IS SILENT, LISTENING, WHILE THE WHOLE EVIL SCHEME OF CONQUEST UNFOLDS.

FINALLY THE KING TURNS TO VAL:- "YOU HAVE ATTENDED MANY OF OUR COUNCILS, SIR QUINTUS, BUT SPEAK NO WORD. HAVE YOU NOTHING TO OFFER?"
1051 3-31-57

HAL FOSTER
"YES, I HAVE, SIRE," ANSWERS VAL, GLANCING SUSPICIOUSLY AROUND THE ROOM, "BUT FOR YOUR EARS ALONE!"
NEXT WEEK:- The Entering Wedge.
©1957, KING FEATURES SYNDICATE, Inc., WORLD RIGHTS RESERVED

Prince Valiant
IN THE DAYS OF KING ARTHUR
BY HAROLD R FOSTER

Our Story: PRINCE VALIANT, ALIAS SIR QUINTUS, RISES AND ANSWERS THE KING'S QUERY. "YES, SIRE, I HAVE A PLAN TO OFFER, BUT FOR YOUR EARS ONLY." AND AS HE SAYS THIS HE GLANCES AROUND THE COUNCIL SUSPICIOUSLY.

WITH A WAVE OF HIS HAND THE KING DISMISSES HIS NOBLES. AND VAL HAS SOWN THE FIRST SEEDS OF JEALOUSY AND DISTRUST.

"AS I RODE HITHER I NOTICED THAT YOUR ARMY HAD LAID WASTE FARM AND PASTURE. HERDS AND FLOCKS MUST BE RESTORED, FIELDS TILLED, THE ARMY FORBIDDEN TO FORAGE."

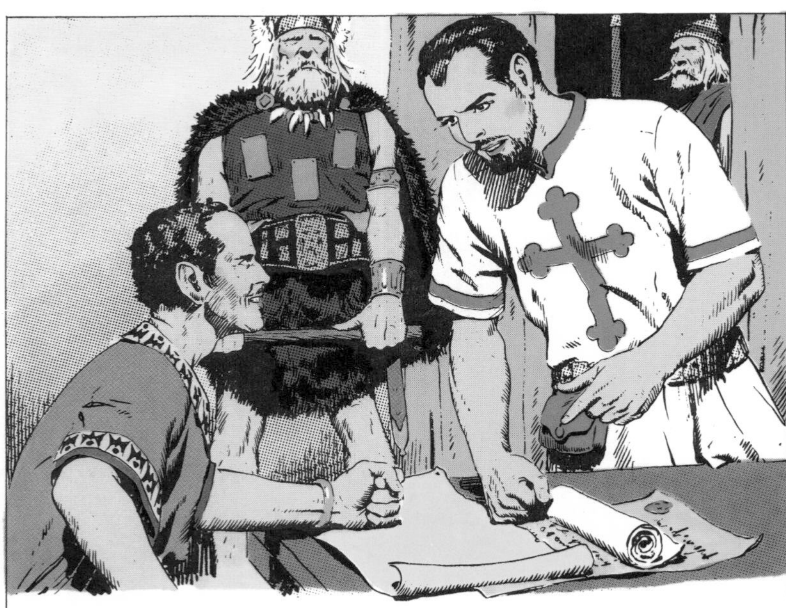
"WHEN I ADVANCE TO CONQUEST I WILL HAVE NO FURTHER USE FOR CORNWALL!" SAYS THE KING COLDLY. "SO THOUGHT ATTILA THE HUN," WARNS VAL. "BUT WHEN HIS HORDES WERE HALTED, THEY STARVED IN A WILDERNESS OF THEIR OWN MAKING!"

"AND YOUR ARMY WILL PAY THE BILL!" SUGGESTS VAL WITH A SLY WINK. "LOOK, SIRE, YOUR SEA RAIDERS PLUNDER THE COASTAL TOWNS AND RETURN TO REST IN THE SAFETY OF YOUR HARBORS WITH RICH LOOT.... LET THEM PAY A TAX FOR THE PRIVILEGE!"

"THEY WILL PAY WILLINGLY, FOR HAVE YOU NOT PROMISED THEM THAT IF THEY MARCH TO VICTORY WITH YOU THEY WILL HAVE ALL BRITAIN TO LOOT?"

KING OCH SYNWYN SITS LOST IN THOUGHT. HE TRUSTS NO ONE, BUT GREED FILLS HIS TWISTED MIND. HOW MUCH CAN HE SQUEEZE FROM HIS WILD FOLLOWERS?
1052 4-7-57

HAL FOSTER
WHEN VAL REACHES HIS CELL-LIKE ROOM THE DOOR HAS BEEN REMOVED. HIS EVERY WORD AND MOVE WILL BE SPIED UPON!
NEXT WEEK- Counterspy.

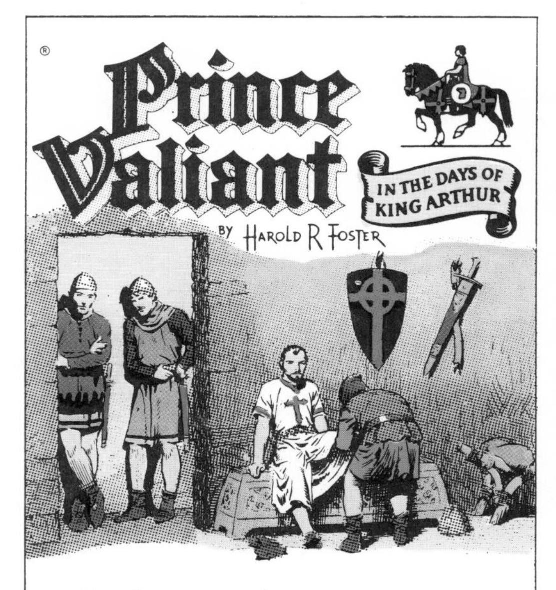

Prince Valiant
IN THE DAYS OF KING ARTHUR
BY HAROLD R FOSTER

Our Story: ON KING OCH SYNWYN'S ORDER THE DOOR TO PRINCE VALIANT'S ROOM IS REMOVED SO HIS EVERY WORD AND MOVE CAN BE SPIED UPON. WELL, VAL CAN USE THESE SAME SPIES FOR HIS OWN PURPOSE.

"FORTUNE SMILES, ALFRED," HE YAWNS. *"SOON WE WILL ALL HAVE RICHES! FOR THE KING IS GOING TO PUT A TAX ON THE LOOT OF HIS RAIDERS!"*

THE RUTHLESS KING WAS EVER CARELESS ABOUT PAYING HIS YEOMEN, SO THIS NEWS IS TOO GOOD TO KEEP. IT SPREADS THROUGH THE CASTLE AND EVEN BEYOND.

BY THE TIME THIS RUMOR REACHES THE CAMP BELOW, IT IS GREATLY EXAGGERATED. THERE ARE ANGRY MUTTERINGS.

BECAUSE THE TAX IS VAL'S SUGGESTION, HE IS MADE COLLECTOR. WITH FIFTY YEOMEN OF THE KING'S GUARD HE GOES THROUGH THE CAMP, ARROGANT AND SNEERING, COLLECTING TAXES AND ENMITY.

THE CART GROANS UNDER THE WEIGHT OF GOLD ARMLETS, SACRED CHURCH ORNAMENTS, JEWELRY AND COINS.

1053 4-14-57

HAL FOSTER

THEN THEY COME TO THE BEACH WHERE HARDY VIKINGS STAND GUARD WITH READY WEAPONS BESIDE THEIR DRAGON SHIPS. NOT ONE COIN OF THEIR HARD-EARNED PLUNDER WILL THEY YIELD. *"I WISH NO TROUBLE; KEEP YOUR TAX MONEY,"* SAYS VAL WITH A GRIN AND A SLY WINK. *"I WILL MAKE THE REST PAY DOUBLE TO MAKE IT UP!"*

NEXT WEEK- The Open Door.

Prince Valiant
IN THE DAYS OF KING ARTHUR
BY HAROLD R FOSTER

Our Story: THE WINTER STORMS ARE OVER, AND EACH DAY MORE RAIDERS COME OVER THE SEA TO JOIN OCH SYNWYN'S ARMY. SOON THIS VICIOUS HORDE WILL BE LOOSED ON PEACEFUL BRITAIN. PRINCE VALIANT MUST ACT FAST.

THE EVIL KING IS PLEASED WITH THE CARTLOAD OF TREASURE HIS TAX COLLECTOR HAS BROUGHT IN, BUT A GREEDY MAN IS NEVER SATISFIED...

"I AM TOLD YOU COLLECTED NOTHING FROM THE VIKINGS." "NO, SIRE," ANSWERS VAL, "HAD I RISKED A FIGHT THIS CART WOULD HAVE BEEN LOOTED DURING THE TURMOIL. WITH YOUR LEAVE I WILL GO BRING THEM TO ORDER."

WITH SOME OF THE YEOMAN GUARD AND THE EVER-PRESENT SPIES, VAL WALKS THROUGH THE CAMP. CRIES OF HATRED, THREATS AND CURSES FOLLOW HIM, FOR IT IS HE WHO COLLECTED THE TAXES; HE WHO PREVENTS THEM FROM SCOURGING THE COUNTRYSIDE!

DOWN BY THE SHIPS HE FINDS A VIKING CAPTAIN. "I WAS BORN IN THULE -- I FAVOR THE NORTHMEN. SO I WARN YOU NOT TO RISK DISASTER TO FURTHER THE AMBITIONS OF A MAD KING. WHY SEEK RICHES ELSEWHERE WHEN THE PLUNDER OF MANY COASTS IS GATHERED IN THIS CAMP? AND YOUR SHIPS ARE READY TO SAIL!"

THE NEXT LARGEST GROUP IS THE BOISTEROUS SCOTTI FROM IRELAND, MERRY RASCALS IMPATIENT FOR ACTION. THEY ARE FRIENDLY, FOR VAL HAD EXCUSED THEM FROM THE TAX, ALSO.
©1957, KING FEATURES SYNDICATE, Inc., WORLD RIGHTS RESERVED.

HAL FOSTER
AS HE LEAVES HE SAYS:- "YOU ARE NOT THE ONLY IMPATIENT ONES, FOR I HEAR THE VIKINGS ARE ABOUT TO COLLECT THEIR WAGES IN ADVANCE AND SAIL AWAY!"
NEXT WEEK-Payday.
1054
4-21-57

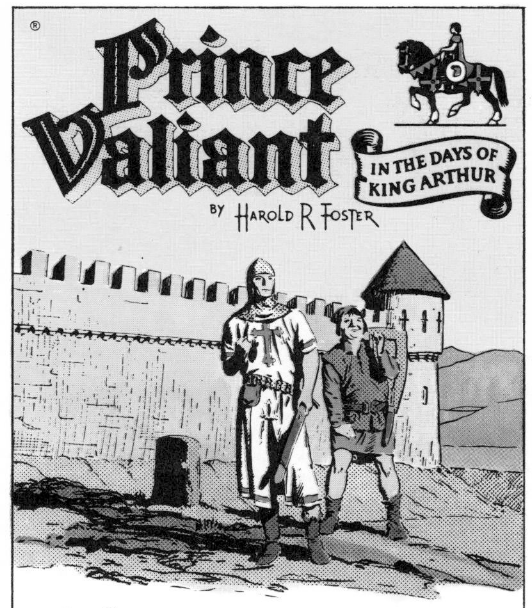

Prince Valiant
IN THE DAYS OF KING ARTHUR
BY HAROLD R FOSTER

Our Story: A CRIMSON SUN IS SETTING TO CLOSE THE DAY UPON WHICH PRINCE VALIANT HAS SACRIFICED HIS HONOR. HE LOOKS BACK ON THE NOISY CAMP AND WONDERS IF THE SEED HE HAS PLANTED WILL BEAR OMINOUS FRUIT.

DOWN BY THE SHORE THE NORTHMEN ARE REPEATING VAL'S WORDS:- *"WHY RISK DISASTER UNDER A MAD KING WHEN THE RICHEST PLUNDER IS RIGHT HERE IN THIS CAMP? MAKE READY THE SHIPS!"*

AND THE IRISH SCOTTI WHISPER:- *"THE NORTHMEN ARE GOING TO COLLECT THEIR WAGES IN ADVANCE ... WHY NOT US? PREPARE TO SAIL!"*

PRINCE VALIANT, ALIAS SIR QUINTUS, RETURNS TO HIS DOORLESS ROOM, AND THE SPIES TAKE THEIR POSITIONS OUTSIDE, MAKING IT IMPOSSIBLE FOR ALFRED TO SHAVE HIS HEAD. BUT ALFRED IS READY:- *"YOUR COLD IS GETTING WORSE, MASTER. YOU MUST KEEP YOUR HEAD COVERED!"*

VAL LAYS ASIDE ARMS AND ARMOR AND APPEARS BEFORE KING OCH. *"SIRE, YOUR TAX HAS DONE TWO THINGS. IT HAS FILLED YOUR EMPTY COFFERS AND IT HAS MADE YOUR ARMY HUNGRY FOR MORE LOOT. THEY GROW RESTLESS AND MUST MARCH AT ONCE!"*

"I GIVE THE ORDERS, SIR QUINTUS," THE SMILING TYRANT REMINDS HIM. *"AND THERE IS A TORTURE CHAMBER FOR THOSE WHO PRESUME TOO FAR."*

HAL FOSTER

BUT WITHIN THE STRONGHOLD SENTRIES ARE REDOUBLED, AND VAL PACES THE WALLS. ALL IS QUIET THROUGH THE LONG NIGHT. THEN, AT THE CHILL HOUR BEFORE DAWN, ANGRY SHOUTS ARE HEARD. LIGHTS APPEAR, THEN FLAMES, AND THE WHOLE CAMP BREAKS INTO AN UPROAR!

NEXT WEEK-**To the Rack!**

1055 4-28-57

Prince Valiant
IN THE DAYS OF KING ARTHUR
BY HAROLD R FOSTER

Our Story: IN THE HOUR BEFORE DAWN THE SEEDS OF GREED PRINCE VALIANT HAS SOWN BEAR FRUIT, AND SWORD AND FLAME BEGIN THE HARVEST. THE MENACING ROAR OF VIOLENCE COMES UP FROM THE CAMP.

AND VAL, ALIAS SIR QUINTUS, ASKS THE OFFICER OF THE GUARD WHY THE KING IS NOT WARNED OF THE MOUNTING DANGER.

"WE DARE NOT RISK THE CERTAIN FATE OF THOSE WHO DISTURB THE KING. HE SLEPT ILL LAST NIGHT AND WENT TO HIS PRISON FOR AMUSEMENT."

THE PRISON GUARDS REFUSE TO UNLOCK THE DOOR. ANY DOOM THAT THREATENS IS BETTER THAN THE KING'S DISPLEASURE!

VAL ARMS HIMSELF AND GOES AMONG THE NOBLES. BECAUSE HE HAS WON THE DUBIOUS FAVOR OF KING OCH, THEY HATE AND ENVY HIM. HOWEVER, IT IS AGREED THAT MEASURES FOR DEFENSE MUST BE TAKEN.

WHEN AT LAST OCH SYNWYN TIRES OF THE AMUSEMENT OF HIS PRISON, THE MORNING IS SPENT, AND THE RIOTING IN THE LOWER CAMP IS AT ITS HEIGHT.

HAL FOSTER

OCH SYNWYN, KING OF CORNWALL, LOOKS UP AS VAL ENTERS. THE HORRIBLE SMILE NEVER LEAVES HIS LIPS, BUT FEAR AND INSANITY GLEAM IN HIS SERPENT EYES AS HE LEAPS BEHIND HIS BODYGUARD. *"SEIZE HIM!"* HE CRIES, *"HE HAS DISOBEYED MY ORDERS AND COME INTO OUR PRESENCE ARMED! TO THE RACK WITH HIM!"*

NEXT WEEK: – The Sortie

1056 5-5-57

Prince Valiant
IN THE DAYS OF KING ARTHUR
BY HAROLD R FOSTER

Our Story: FROM THE PROTECTION OF HIS BODYGUARD, OCH SYNWYN, KING OF CORNWALL, SCREAMS AT PRINCE VAL:- *"AGAINST MY ORDERS YOU HAVE COME INTO MY PRESENCE ARMED. SEIZE HIM AND PLACE HIM ON THE RACK!"*

"UNLESS YOU ATTEND TO OUR DEFENSES THERE WILL BE NO KING AT DAY'S END!" ANSWERS VAL.

ONLY THEN DOES THE KING LEARN THAT HIS ARMY CAMP IS ABLAZE WITH VIOLENCE. *"YOU STARTED THIS WITH YOUR TAXES! NOW STOP IT!"* HE QUAVERS.

NOW THAT VAL IS WITHOUT KNIGHTLY HONOR, HAVING SWORN A FALSE OATH, HE WISHES ONLY TO DIE FIGHTING. BUT BEFORE HE DOES HE WANTS TO DESTROY, IF POSSIBLE, THE ARMY OF CUTTHROATS THE KING HAS PLANNED TO LET LOOSE ON BRITAIN.

THE DISCIPLINED YEOMEN SLASH INTO THE LEADERLESS MOB, DRIVING THEM BACK. VAL DOES NOT FALL; HE IS TOO WELL TRAINED IN WINNING BATTLES, AND ANOTHER PLAN HAS JUST COME TO HIM!

ALFRED IS SENT SCAMPERING BACK ACROSS A BATTLEFIELD LITTERED WITH THE PLUNDER OF COUNTLESS RAIDS.

AND SOON HAS THE HOUSE SERVANTS HURRYING BACK AND FORTH COLLECTING THIS VAST TREASURE.

1057 5-12-57

HAL FOSTER

VAL HAS LED HIS TROOP AS FAR AS THEY CAN GO WITHOUT BEING SURROUNDED. HE COMMANDS AN ORDERLY RETREAT.

NEXT WEEK - The King's Playthings.

Prince Valiant
IN THE DAYS OF KING ARTHUR
BY HAROLD R FOSTER

Our Story: NEVER HAD KING OCH DREAMED THERE WAS SUCH WEALTH AS HIS SERVANTS BRING IN FROM THE BATTLEFIELD. IT IS ENOUGH TO COMPENSATE HIM FOR THE LOSS OF HIS ARMY AND HIS VISIONS OF CONQUEST.

PRINCE VALIANT AND HIS TROOP RETREAT SLOWLY, AND THE MOB, STILL FIGHTING AMONG THEMSELVES, ARE UNABLE TO ORGANIZE AN EFFECTIVE COUNTERATTACK BEFORE THE SHELTER OF THE CASTLE IS REACHED.

THE SORTIE AND THE LOOTING OF THEIR CAMP TURN THE SULLEN ANGER OF THE ARMY TOWARD THE CASTLE, AND SOON CATAPULT AND SPRINGAL ARE HURLING THEIR MISSILES OVER THE WALL.

THE KEEPER OF THE PRISON KEYS IS NO LONGER ABLE TO DENY VAL ADMITTANCE. QUICKLY HE TAKES THE KEYS AND ENTERS.

THE KING'S ASSISTANT TORTURERS SEE A STRANGER ENTER. PEOPLE IN THEIR PROFESSION HAVE NO FRIENDS, SO THEY ATTACK. WHILE IN THE KING'S EMPLOY THEY ALSO LEARNED THAT DEATH IS OFTEN A BLESSED RELIEF FROM PAIN. VAL PROVES THIS QUICKLY.

THEN HE UNLOCKS THE CELL DOORS AND TELLS ALL WHO ARE STILL ABLE TO UNDERSTAND THAT THE DOORS MUST BE KEPT CLOSED UNTIL THE RIGHT TIME. THEN HE STAGGERS OUT.

USED AS HE IS TO THE BRUTALITY OF WAR, THE SIGHT OF THE MAIMED AND TORTURED VICTIMS OF THE KING'S VINDICTIVENESS WILL LIVE WITH HIM EVER.

1058. 5-19-57

HAL FOSTER

AS THE DAY ENDS SO DOES THE RIOTING AND CONFUSION IN THE CAMP. IT IS PLAIN THAT THE ARMY HAS ACCEPTED COMPETENT LEADERSHIP.

NEXT WEEK- **A Scream is heard.**

Prince Valiant
IN THE DAYS OF KING ARTHUR
BY HAROLD R FOSTER

Our Story: THE ARMY THAT WAS RECRUITED TO PLUNDER ALL BRITAIN FINDS A LEADER AND ORGANIZES AN ATTACK ON THE CASTLE OF ITS ONE-TIME MASTER.

AND THAT MASTER, KING OCH SYNWYN, IS SMILING DOWN ON THE AGONY OF ONE OF HIS SOLDIERS! HE RUBS COLD HANDS TOGETHER, PITILESS AND UNMOVED BY THE SUFFERING OF MEN.

HE IS DRAWN IRRESISTIBLY TO HIS PRISON AND IS ANNOYED THAT HE MUST UNLOCK THE DOOR HIMSELF.

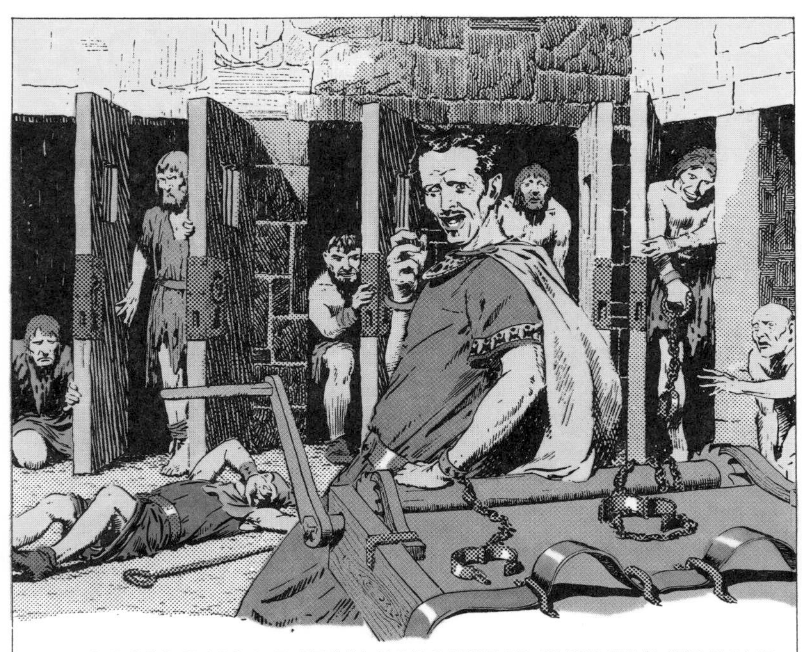
HIS POOR, TWISTED BRAIN DOES NOT AT ONCE REALIZE WHAT IS HAPPENING. THEN HE SCREAMS AS THE CELL DOORS SLOWLY OPEN AND HIS VICTIMS WALK, STAGGER OR CRAWL OUT. AGAIN AND AGAIN HE SCREAMS!

BUT NO ONE HEARS HIM, FOR THE ATTACK ON THE WALLS IS BEING PRESSED FIERCELY.

THE ARMY IS IN POSSESSION OF THE WAR MACHINES BUILT FOR THE CONQUEST OF BRITAIN, AND ALL NIGHT, BY THE LIGHT OF BONFIRES, THEY THUNDER AT THE WALLS.

AND WITHIN THOSE CRUMBLING WALLS VAL IS OUTLINING A DARING PLAN.
"YOU KNOW WHAT MANNER OF MEN COMPOSE THE ARMY," HE CONCLUDES. "OUR LAND WILL KNOW NO PEACE OR SAFETY UNLESS IT IS DESTROYED TO THE LAST MAN, NO MATTER WHAT THE COST!"
1059 5-26-57

HAL FOSTER
ALL THROUGH THE NIGHT PREPARATIONS ARE MADE FOR ONE LAST GAMBLE.
NEXT WEEK-The Price of Victory.

Prince Valiant
IN THE DAYS OF KING ARTHUR
BY HAROLD R FOSTER
Our Story: OCH SYNWYN, KING OF CORNWALL, SHARES A CLOAK WITH HIS TWO WARDENS, UNNOTICED, WHILE INTO A DUNGEON BENEATH THE PRISON FLOOR GOES THE VAST TREASURE PRINCE VALIANT HAS CAPTURED.

THEN THE COVER IS SEALED AND PROTECTED WITH A LAYER OF EARTH. VAL HIMSELF APPLIES THE TORCH THAT WILL DESTROY THIS LOATHSOME BUILDING.

AT DAWN THE CASTLE GATES SWING WIDE AND VAL LEADS THE MOUNTED KNIGHTS IN A THUNDEROUS CHARGE.

AND THROUGH THE GAP COME THE BAGGAGE WAGONS WITH THE WOMEN AND CHILDREN, PROTECTED BY THE YEOMEN AND HEADED FOR THE OPEN COUNTRY AT A GALLOP.

THERE IS NO PURSUIT. FOR VAL HAS CORRECTLY ESTIMATED THEIR ENEMIES. TRAINED ONLY FOR PILLAGE AND DESTRUCTION, THEY STRUGGLE TO BE FIRST THROUGH THE OPEN GATES.

THEN FOLLOWS AN ORGY OF LOOTING AND DESTRUCTION.

1060 6-2-57

HAL FOSTER
IN THEIR SEARCH FOR PLUNDER IT IS ONLY A MATTER OF TIME BEFORE THE WINE CELLAR IS DISCOVERED.
NEXT WEEK - The End of Sir Quintus.

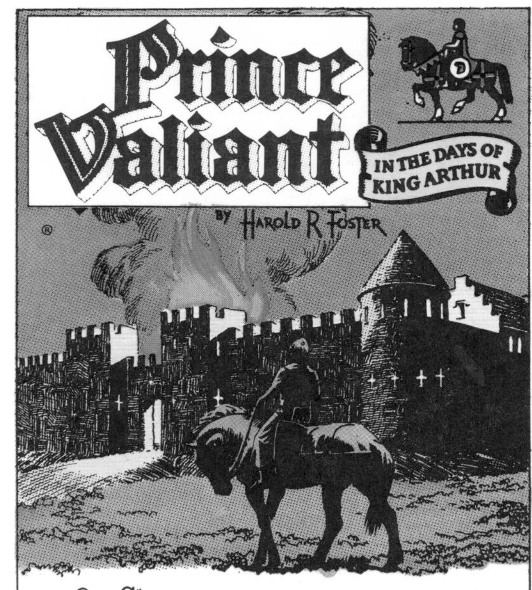
Prince Valiant
IN THE DAYS OF KING ARTHUR
BY HAROLD R FOSTER
Our Story: IN THE DARKNESS PRINCE VALIANT RIDES RIGHT UP TO THE CASTLE WALLS. BY THE LIGHT OF THE BURNING PRISON HE CAN SEE THE GATES WIDE OPEN, NO SENTRIES ON THE WALL. FROM WITHIN COMES THE SOUND OF WILD CAROUSING.

IT DID NOT TAKE LONG FOR THIS ARMY TO DESTROY EVERYTHING OF WORTH WITHIN THE CAPTURED CASTLE. NOR WILL THE WINE CELLAR ESCAPE DESTRUCTION ERE MORNING.

VAL ASSIGNS EACH CAPTAIN HIS PART. *"WE ARE STILL OUTNUMBERED TEN TO ONE; SOME OF US WILL NOT SEE TOMORROW'S SUN. BUT WE HAVE A DUTY TO DO. ONLY WHEN THIS ARMY IS DESTROYED WILL OUR LAND BE SAFE!"*

THE RISING SUN SEES THE CASTLE REGAINED, THE LAND SAVED. VAL SHEATHES HIS SWORD. HIS MISSION IS FULFILLED. BUT NO FEELING OF JOY IS HIS; FOR HE HAS PRACTICED DECEIT, ASSUMED A FALSE NAME, SWORN A FALSE OATH, AND IN SO DOING LOST HIS KNIGHTLY HONOR!

THE TREASURE TAKEN FROM THE ARMY WILL RESTORE THE CASTLE AND THE KINGDOM, BUT AS THE DAYS PASS ONE QUESTION REMAINS UNANSWERED: *"WHAT HAS BECOME OF SIR QUINTUS?"*

AND SO A LEGEND IS BORN, THE LEGEND OF SIR QUINTUS WHO APPEARED FROM NOWHERE, RID THE KINGDOM OF KING OCH AND HIS TERRIBLE ARMY, THEN AS MYSTERIOUSLY VANISHED.
6-9-57

HAL FOSTER

SIR QUINTUS RIDES INTO TINTAGEL, WHERE ALFRED, WITH THE AID OF A RAZOR, MAKES HIM DISAPPEAR FOREVER, AND PRINCE VALIANT TAKES HIS PLACE.

NEXT WEEK–Camelot.

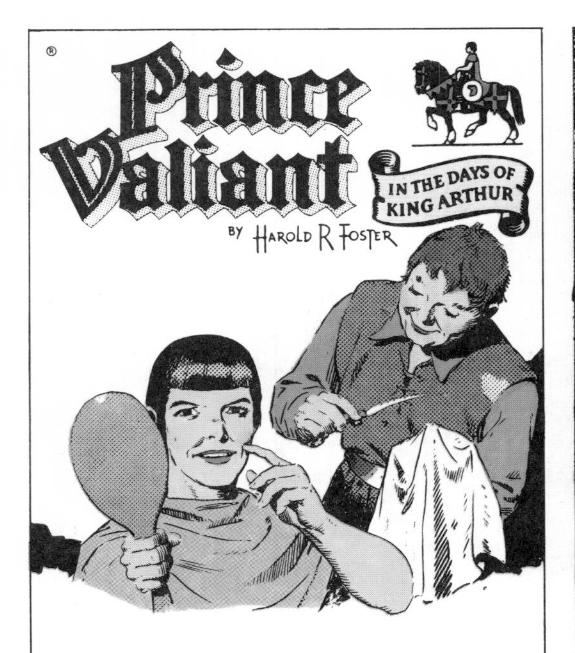
Prince Valiant
IN THE DAYS OF KING ARTHUR
BY HAROLD R FOSTER
Our Story: A FEW DEFT STROKES OF A RAZOR AND SIR QUINTUS VANISHES AND PRINCE VALIANT IS ONCE MORE HIM-SELF.... ALMOST.

AH, HOW GOOD IT IS TO ONCE MORE WEAR THE RED STALLION CREST AND BUCKLE ON THE 'SINGING SWORD'!

VAL REPORTS HIS ADVENTURES TO SIR BEAUMAINS, THE COMMANDANT AT TINTAGEL: "NOW THAT KING OCH SYNWYN IS DEAD AND HIS ARMY CRUSHED, THE REMAINING KINGS WILL OFFER LITTLE TROUBLE."

TO MAKE SURE, A DOZEN ARMED KNIGHTS AND A HUNDRED MOUNTED YEOMEN SET OUT TO PAY A FRIENDLY, IF THREAT-ENING, VISIT.

BELOW THE 'IRON GATE' A SHIP AWAITS, AS VAL BIDS FARE-WELL TO THE FRIENDS WHO HOLD LONELY TINTAGEL IN KING ARTHUR'S NAME.

VAL AND ALFRED LAND AT BRISTOL AND ONCE MORE GO THROUGH THE TEDIOUS BUSINESS OF PURCHASING MOUNTS.
©1957, KING FEATURES SYNDICATE, Inc., WORLD RIGHTS RESERVED.

HAL FOSTER
FAR OUT ON THE PLAIN OF SALISBURY THE RUINS OF AN ANCIENT TEMPLE STAND, GLOWING STARK AND SILENT IN THE RAYS OF THE SETTING SUN. VAL WOULD FAIN HAVE ENTERED, BUT THE HORSES ARE WILD WITH FEAR AND REFUSE TO APPROACH.
NEXT WEEK- Stonehenge
1062 6·16·57

Prince Valiant
IN THE DAYS OF KING ARTHUR
BY HAROLD R. FOSTER

Our Story: PRINCE VALIANT AND ALFRED SPEND THE NIGHT AMONG THE OAKS WHERE THE SACRED MISTLETOE GROWS. THEY TAKE TURNS ON WATCH, FOR THIS IS A MYSTERIOUS PLACE.

AT DAWN VAL RETURNS TO THE TEMPLE ALONE, FOR NEITHER HORSE NOR SQUIRE WOULD ENTER THE RUINS. LEGENDS TELL OF ANCIENT DRUID RITES AND OF A CURSE THAT LIES UPON IT.

WITH A FEELING OF AWE VAL WANDERS ABOUT THE RUINS. HE STOPS BEFORE THE ALTAR STONE ..... IT STILL BEARS SIGNS OF RECENT SACRIFICE, AND THE GRASS IS TRAMPLED AS IF BY A MULTITUDE OF FEET!

HE IS STARTLED BY A WOMAN'S VOICE :— *"INTRUDERS ARE NOT WELCOME HERE. GO, AND DO NOT RETURN. THERE WAS ONE WHO HEEDED NOT OUR WARNING. HE LIES YONDER!"*

AND IN THE DIRECTION THE PRIESTESS HAD POINTED VAL FINDS THE BODY OF A MAN. ON HIS WRIST IS A HEAVY-KNOTTED WHIP, AND TO HIS HEELS ARE FASTENED AWFUL SPURS ..... A 'HORSE KILLER'!

HAVING NO TOOLS FOR DIGGING, VAL AND ALFRED BURY HIM BENEATH A CAIRN OF STONES. THEN VAL SEES THE HORSE, GLEAMING RED IN THE SUN.

HAL FOSTER

EVEN THOUGH THE EYES ARE WILD WITH FEAR, THE MOUTH TWISTED BY A CRUEL BIT; EVEN THOUGH THE FLANKS ARE RIPPED AND SCARRED, IT IS THE MOST SPLENDID STALLION VAL HAS EVER SEEN. *"I MUST HAVE THAT HORSE!"*

NEXT WEEK- **The Failure**

1063 6-23-57

Prince Valiant
IN THE DAYS OF KING ARTHUR
BY HAROLD R FOSTER

Our Story: PRINCE VALIANT LOOKS AT THE GREAT RED STALLION. "OH, YOU BEAUTY," HE WHISPERS, AND ADVANCES SLOWLY WITH CARESSING WORDS.

BUT WITH A SQUEAL OF FEAR THE SPLENDID BEAST THUNDERS AWAY ACROSS THE PLAIN.

ALL DAY LONG VAL TRIES, IN EVERY WAY HE KNOWS, TO CAPTURE HIM, BUT TO NO AVAIL. AT SUNDOWN, HE ADMITS DEFEAT.

NEXT DAY, AS THE JOURNEY TO CAMELOT IS RESUMED, VAL LOOKS BACK. FAR OUT ON THE PLAIN THE STALLION IS TRYING TO FEED DESPITE THE CRUEL BIT FROM WHICH HE CANNOT ESCAPE.

CAMELOT ONCE MORE, PERHAPS FOR THE LAST TIME! FOR VAL MUST CONFESS THAT HE IS NOW WITHOUT HONOR, UNWORTHY TO HANG HIS SHIELD IN THE HALL OF CHAMPIONS OR SIT AT THE ROUND TABLE.

HE AVOIDS MEETING FRIENDS. THIS IS EASY, FOR IT IS SPRING AND MOST OF THEM HAVE GONE TO THEIR FIEFS TO SUPERINTEND THE PLANTING.

SIR KAY, THE SENESCHAL, IS REQUESTED TO GET VAL AN AUDIENCE WITH THE KING.
6-30-57

HAL FOSTER

KING ARTHUR IS JOYFUL. "SO THE MERRY SIR VALIANT HAS RETURNED! AND VICTORIOUS TOO, I'LL WAGER. THIS CALLS FOR A SIEGE OF THE ROUND TABLE THAT HE MAY TELL US OF HIS HIGH ADVENTURES!"

NEXT WEEK-An Affair of Honor.

Prince Valiant
IN THE DAYS OF KING ARTHUR
BY HAROLD R FOSTER
Our Story: PRINCE VALIANT HAD HOPED TO TELL OF HIS DISGRACE TO THE KING IN PRIVATE, AND AS PRIVATELY LEAVE CAMELOT FOREVER. BUT NOW HE MUST TELL ALL AT A SIEGE OF THE ROUND TABLE!

VAL REFUSES TO TAKE HIS SEAT. "WHEN YOU HEAR MY TALE YOU WILL NOT WISH ME ONE OF YOUR COMPANY!"

THEN HE RELATES HOW, UNDER A FALSE NAME, HE TOOK THE OATH OF FEALTY TO KING OCH SYNWYN AND BY TRICKERY CAUSED THE DESTRUCTION OF THE KING AND HIS EVIL ARMY.

NOW KING ARTHUR ARISES SAYING: "ALL HONOR TO A KNIGHT SO FAITHFUL THAT HE WOULD RISK LIFE AND HONOR TO SERVE HIS KING, AND WHO, ALONE, SAVED THE REALM FROM RUINOUS WAR! BE SEATED, SIR VALIANT!"

BUT VAL IS STUBBORN. "'TWAS ONLY MY DUTY TO CARRY OUT MY MISSION, SIRE, BUT IN SO DOING ....." "TUT, TUT!" INTERRUPTS THE KING, GROWING ANGRY. "YOU DID BUT INCREASE YOUR HONOR. SIT DOWN, LAD! DON'T BE STUBBORN, SIT DOWN!"

"I WON'T SIT DOWN!" SHOUTS VAL, GROWING RED IN THE FACE. "NO KING CAN TELL ME WRONG IS RIGHT!"

"THEN STAND UP, FOR ALL I CARE!" ROARS THE KING. "YOU STIFF-NECKED, TOPLOFTY, PLASTER SAINT!"
©1957, KING FEATURES SYNDICATE, Inc., WORLD RIGHTS RESERVED.

HAL FOSTER
ARTHUR SITS DOWN, DRAINS HIS GOBLET AND GLARES AT PRINCE VAL TO HIDE A GROWING FEAR. THE FEAR THAT HE MIGHT LOSE THIS HEAD-STRONG, LOVABLE, MOST GALLANT KNIGHT.
NEXT WEEK-The Gift.
1065
7-7-57

Prince Valiant
IN THE DAYS OF KING ARTHUR
BY HAROLD R FOSTER
Our Story: PRINCE VALIANT REFUSES TO TAKE HIS PLACE AT THE ROUND TABLE. ALTHOUGH HE HAS SAVED THE REALM FROM A COSTLY WAR, HE CLAIMS THAT IN SO DOING HE HAS LOST HIS HONOR. STUBBORNLY HE REJECTS ALL ARGUMENT AND EVEN QUARRELS WITH HIS KING!

HIS EYES GROW MISTY AS HE LOOKS AROUND.... NEVERMORE WILL HE BE ONE OF THIS GALLANT COMPANY... BRAVE, SCARRED WARRIORS ALL. OR SO HE THINKS UNTIL THE KING RISES...

"BEFORE SUCH STUBBORNNESS EVEN YOUR KING MUST ADMIT DEFEAT. BUT THAT SO STEADFAST A SERVANT OF THE CROWN BE NOT UNREWARDED, I PLACE IN SIR VALIANT'S KEEPING A TENTH PART OF MY HONOR!"

THEN THE KNIGHTS OF THE ROUND TABLE, TO A MAN, RISE AND PLEDGE A PORTION OF THEIR HONOR TO VAL'S SAFEKEEPING.

VAL TAKES HIS PLACE, AND TEARS COME UNASHAMED. FOR TO THESE KNIGHTS HONOR IS A SACRED THING, MORE PRECIOUS THAN LIFE ITSELF!

HAL FOSTER
QUIETLY KING ARTHUR RETIRES. FOR WELL HE KNOWS HIS LUSTY KNIGHTS. WITH SIR VALIANT ONCE MORE RESTORED TO HIS GAY AND WITTY SELF, AND GAWAIN ALWAYS READY FOR A FIGHT OR FROLIC, THIS SIEGE WILL LAST TILL DAWN!
NEXT WEEK- The Red Stallion
1066
7-14-57

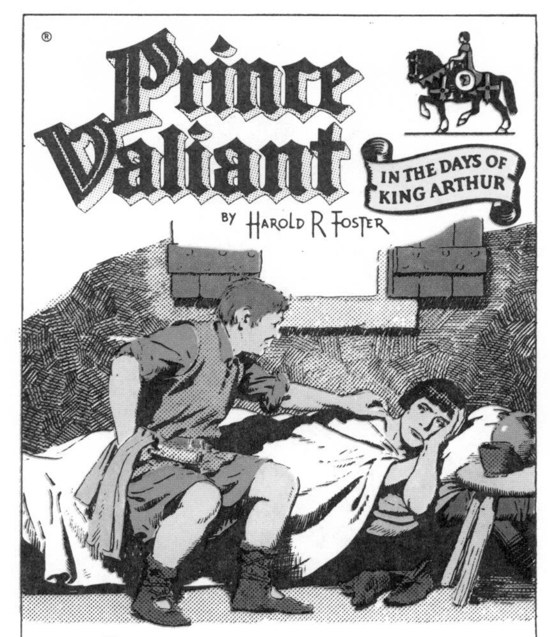
Prince Valiant
IN THE DAYS OF KING ARTHUR
BY HAROLD R FOSTER

Our Story: THE SIEGE OF THE ROUND TABLE ROARED TO A LUSTY FINISH, AND PART OF THE WRECKAGE TURNS OUT TO BE PRINCE VALIANT!

"I'LL WAGER A PAGE BOY WITH A STICK COULD WHIP THE ENTIRE FELLOWSHIP OF TABLE ROUND THIS DAY!" MUMBLES VAL, TRYING DESPERATELY TO CURE HIS INDIGESTION.

"THE PITFALLS OF CAMELOT ARE TOO MANY FOR A WEAKLING SUCH AS I. MAKE READY THE HORSES AND WE WILL TRY FOR THAT WILD STALLION."

FROM THE GREAT STABLES AT CAMELOT, FAST-RUNNING HORSES ARE SELECTED AND EQUIPMENT CAREFULLY CHOSEN. FOR VAL HAS SET HIS HEART ON OWNING THE RED STALLION.

ALL DAY LONG HE CANTERS ACROSS SALISBURY PLAIN SEARCHING FOR HIS PRIZE. THEN, AS HE CIRCLES THE RUINED TEMPLE CALLED STONEHENGE.....

.....HE SEES THE HORSE! IT IS NIBBLING OAT CAKES, AND FROM A DISTANCE THE DRUID PRIESTESS IS SPEAKING TO IT SOFTLY.

"CAN SOFT WORDS AND OAT CAKES WIN HIM?" ASKS VAL AS HE RIDES UP. "HE IS STILL A MAN-KILLER," ANSWERS THE GIRL. "THE PAIN OF THAT CRUEL BIT REMINDS HIM OF MAN'S BRUTALITY."

1067 7-21-57

HAL FOSTER

"FREE HIM OF THAT BIT AND BRIDLE AND YOU MIGHT TAME HIM. IF YOU DARE!"

NEXT WEEK- The Making of a Man-Killer

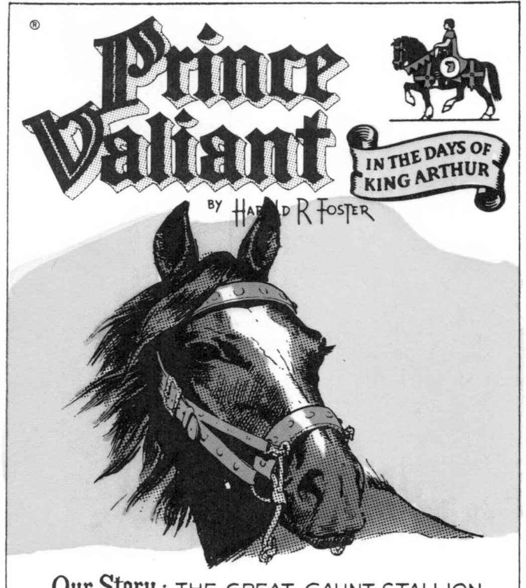
Prince Valiant
IN THE DAYS OF KING ARTHUR
BY HAROLD R FOSTER
Our Story: THE GREAT, GAUNT STALLION TESTS THE AIR WITH SENSITIVE NOSTRILS. MEN ARE NEAR..... AND OTHER HORSES. FOR AGES HE AND HIS KIND HAVE BEEN THE SERVANTS AND COMPANIONS OF MAN. IMPELLED BY A STRANGE LONGING HE DRAWS NEAR, BUT NOT TOO NEAR.

FOR HE REMEMBERS HOW, AS A COLT, HE HAD BEEN TRAINED WITH GENTLE FIRMNESS UNTIL THAT AWFUL DAY.....

.....WHEN HE HAD FALLEN INTO THE HANDS OF THAT BRUTAL MASTER WHO MUST BEND EVERYTHING TO HIS WILL.

THEN CAME THE TIME WHEN HIS MASTER TRIED TO FORCE HIM INTO A TEMPLE BECAUSE IT WAS FORBIDDEN, AND THEY HAD FOUGHT IT OUT; THE MAN'S WHIP, SPURS, BIT AND WILL AGAINST THE STALLION'S SPIRIT.

AND THE MAN HAD TIED HIM TO A TREE AND CUT A CUDGEL TO BREAK, ONCE AND FOR ALL, THAT BRAVE SPIRIT.

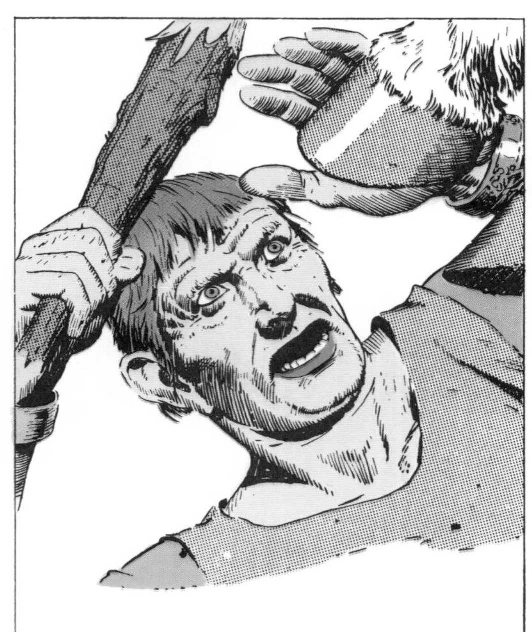
IN THAT HOUR THE STALLION HAD BECOME A MAN-KILLER.

THIS IS THE HORSE THAT PRINCE VALIANT IS PREPARING TO CATCH.

HAL FOSTER
AT DAWN OF A WARM SPRING DAY THE CHASE BEGINS.
NEXT WEEK- Man against Man-Killer.

1068 7-28-57

Prince Valiant
IN THE DAYS OF KING ARTHUR
BY HAROLD R FOSTER
Our Story: PRINCE VALIANT HAS SET HIS HEART ON BEING THE OWNER OF THE RED STALLION. BUT AS LONG AS THE SPUR WOUNDS PAIN HIS FLANKS AND THE CRUEL BRIDLE MAKES GRAZING AN AGONY THE SPLENDID OUTLAW WILL REMAIN A MAN-KILLER.

AT FIRST THE GREAT BEAST EASILY OUT-DISTANCES HIS PURSUERS, BUT VAL AND HIS HELPERS CHANGE OFTEN TO FRESH MOUNTS.

ALL DAY LONG AND ALL THROUGH THE NIGHT THE CHASE CONTINUES, FOR THE STALLION MUST NOT BE ALLOWED TO REST OR DRINK.

AT LAST THE TIME ARRIVES FOR THE CAPTURE OF THE TIRED PRIZE.

AND VAL MUST GO IN AMONG THE DESPERATELY THRASHING HOOFS TO SECURE A HOBBLE.

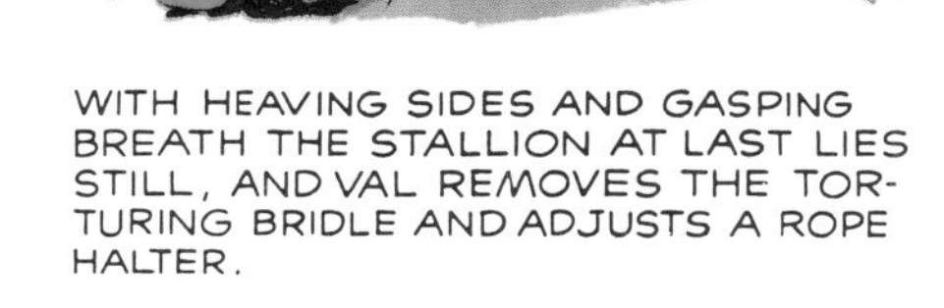
WITH HEAVING SIDES AND GASPING BREATH THE STALLION AT LAST LIES STILL, AND VAL REMOVES THE TOR-TURING BRIDLE AND ADJUSTS A ROPE HALTER.
1069 8-4-57

HAL FOSTER
ONE LAST EFFORT IT MAKES TO REMAIN A MAN-KILLER, AND ALMOST SUCCEEDS.
NEXT WEEK - The Oat Cake.

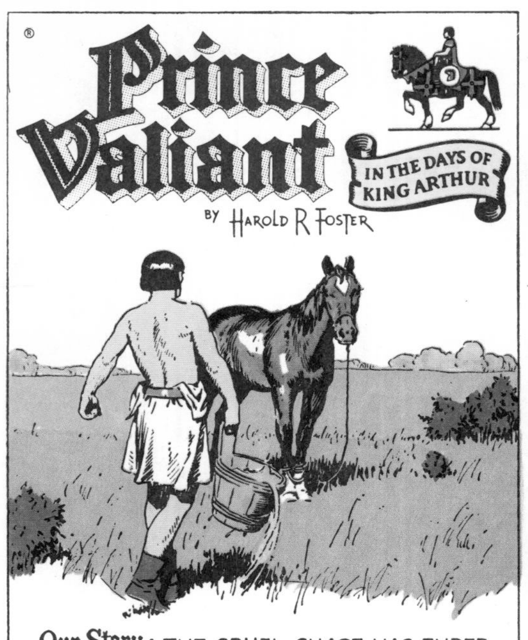
Prince Valiant
IN THE DAYS OF KING ARTHUR
BY HAROLD R FOSTER
Our Story: THE CRUEL CHASE HAS ENDED AND THE GREAT RED STALLION STANDS EXHAUSTED, HALTERED AND HOBBLED. PRINCE VALIANT BRINGS WATER TO WHERE HE IS PASTURED.

AS THE WOUNDS INFLICTED BY HIS FORMER MASTER HEAL, THE STALLION BECOMES ALMOST GENTLE. NOT SO WITH ALFRED! HE IS NOT USED TO SO MUCH RIDING AND WILL DINE STANDING FOR MANY A DAY.

BUT MANY A DAY WILL PASS ERE THEY DARE VENTURE TO PUT ON SADDLE OR BRIDLE.

WHENEVER HIS FORMER MASTER GOT IN THE SADDLE THE HORSE EXPECTED THE PAIN OF WHIP AND SPUR. HE MAKES ONE MORE TRY FOR FREEDOM, AND ONLY BY A MIRACLE DOES VAL RETAIN HIS SEAT!

THEN HE BOLTS, RACING ACROSS THE PLAIN, GREAT STRIDES EATING UP THE MILES. VAL LETS HIM RUN HIS FILL, THEN GENTLY BUT MASTERFULLY BRINGS HIM UNDER CONTROL.

AS HE CANTERS BY THE RUINS OF STONE-HENGE, VAL SEES THE DRUID PRIESTESS STANDING, HAND OUTSTRETCHED. HE SLACKENS THE REINS. THIS IS THE FINAL TEST.

THE VELVET MUZZLE REACHES OUT AND ALMOST DAINTILY TAKES THE OFFERED OAT CAKE. "YOU HAVE TRULY WON YOUR PRIZE," SHE SAYS. "HAD YOU BEEN LESS GENTLE I WOULD HAVE FREED HIM IN THE NIGHT!"
1070
8-11-57

HAL FOSTER
IT IS A JOYFUL OCCASION, AND SHORTLY THEREAFTER A STABLE HAND, A PRINCE AND A SQUIRE MAKE MERRY AT A VICTORY FEAST.
NEXT WEEK- Disputed Ownership

Prince Valiant
IN THE DAYS OF KING ARTHUR
BY HAROLD R FOSTER

Our Story: NEVER BEFORE HAS PRINCE VALIANT BEEN SO SPLENDIDLY MOUNTED. AS THEY NEAR CAMELOT HE GIVES A SHOUT AND RACES ACROSS THE GREEN.....

.....AND ENTERS THE MERLIN GATE AT FULL GALLOP, ELATED AS A SCHOOL-BOY WITH A NEW TOY!

TWICE AROUND THE PRACTICE YARD HE CANTERS, SCATTERING THE KNIGHTS AT THEIR TRAINING. THEN HAPPILY HE LEADS HIS RED STALLION OFF TO THE STABLES.

VAL IS TELLING THE OTHER KNIGHTS OF HIS CONQUEST OVER THE RED MAN-KILLER. *"WHAT SPIRITED HORSE WOULD NOT BE A KILLER WHEN SUBJECTED TO THIS CRUELTY?"* AND AS HE SHOWS THE PRONGED SPURS AND CRUEL BRIDLE A VOICE INTERRUPTS:-

"THAT IS MY FATHER'S BRIDLE, THOSE ARE HIS SPURS... THAT HORSE IS RIGHTLY MINE!"

"AND WOULD YOU USE THESE INSTRUMENTS OF TORTURE ON HIM AS YOUR FATHER DID?" ASKS VAL.

"BY YOUR OWN WORDS THAT HORSE KILLED MY FATHER. A LIFE FOR A LIFE! IN JUSTICE I MUST KILL THAT HORSE!"

"GIVE HIM UP TO ME OR I BRAND YOU AS A COMMON HORSE THIEF!"

"LIKE YOUR FATHER, YOU SEEM TO BE A BRAVE KILLER OF HORSES, BUT DID YOU EVER OFFER HARM TO A MAN?"

1071 8-18-57

HAL FOSTER

VAL'S EYES ARE HARD WITH MOUNTING ANGER, BUT HE SAYS CALMLY: *"WITHIN THE HOUR I RIDE TO THE MEADOWS, ARMED. THE STEED I RIDE IS FOR HIM WHO IS MAN ENOUGH TO TAKE IT!"*

NEXT WEEK - The Duel.

Prince Valiant
IN THE DAYS OF KING ARTHUR
BY HAROLD R FOSTER

Our Story: SADOR SHAKES HIS FIST AT PRINCE VALIANT. "THAT RED STALLION IS RIGHTLY MINE..... IF I MAY NOT HAVE HIM NO ONE SHALL!" HE SHOUTS. THEN HE ARMS HIMSELF TO MAKE GOOD HIS BOAST.

WITH MOUNTING ANGER VAL PREPARES FOR COMBAT. THE SENSELESS BRUTALITY OF SADOR, WHO WOULD WREAK VENGEANCE ON A HORSE, HAS AROUSED HIS WRATH.

VAL CALMS THE GREAT STALLION WITH SOOTHING WORDS WHILE HE IS BEING SADDLED, FOR IT WILL YET BE MANY A LONG DAY ERE THE SPLENDID HORSE FORGETS MAN'S CRUELTY.

WHEN VAL REACHES THE MEADOWS SADOR IS ALREADY THERE, WAITING. MANY KNIGHTS HAVE RIDDEN OUT FROM CAMELOT TO SEE THE CONTEST, AMONG THEM SIR GAWAIN. "WARE THIS SADOR," HE CAUTIONS. "HE IS A HARDY WARRIOR, BUT TREACHEROUS!"

WITHOUT WAITING FOR THE SIGNAL TO BEGIN, SADOR CHARGES. TO VAL'S HORROR THE POINT OF THE LANCE IS AIMED AT THE RED STALLION'S THROAT!

THE ANGRY ROAR OF THE ONLOOKERS TURNS TO SHOUTS OF APPROVAL AS VAL'S LANCE CLUBS HIS OPPONENT'S ASIDE.

SADOR WHEELS, AND CRUEL SPURS RIP HIS MOUNT'S FLANKS IN A SUDDEN CHARGE.

1072 8-25-57

HAL FOSTER
AGAIN THE GLEAMING SPEAR-POINT IS AIMED AT THE BROAD CHEST OF VAL'S CHARGER!
NEXT WEEK–Val Disarmed

Prince Valiant
IN THE DAYS OF KING ARTHUR
BY HAROLD R FOSTER
Our Story: SADOR WHEELS AND CHARGES, HOPING TO CATCH PRINCE VALIANT OFF GUARD. AGAIN THE SHARP LANCE POINT AIMS AT THE RED STALLION'S BREAST IN HIS DETERMINATION TO DESTROY THE HORSE THAT KILLED HIS BRUTAL FATHER.

VAL CIRCLES AND COMES IN, HIS LANCE HELD HIGH. INSTEAD OF STRAIGHTENING OUT FOR THE RIGHT HAND PASS, HE CROSSES OVER TO THE LEFT.

HE BRINGS HIS LANCE DOWN ACROSS HIS MOUNT'S NECK. THE SUDDEN MANEUVER DOES NOT GIVE TIME FOR ACCURATE AIM, BUT IT CATCHES SADOR OFF GUARD.

VAL IS OUT OF THE SADDLE AND RACING TOWARD HIS ENEMY BEFORE HE CAN REMOUNT.

SADOR FIGHTS DEFENSIVELY, CIRCLING, RETREATING, GETTING EVER NEARER THE RED STALLION.

SUDDENLY HE TURNS, AND WITH UPRAISED SWORD, RUNS TOWARD THE OBJECT OF HIS HATRED.
KING FEATURES SYNDICATE, Inc., WORLD RIGHTS RESERVED

TOO LATE TO CATCH HIM, VAL FLINGS THE 'SINGING SWORD' AT THE SWIFTLY MOVING LEGS.
1073
9-1-57

HAL FOSTER
VAL STANDS UNARMED, WHILE SADOR STRUGGLES TO HIS FEET. HE PLACES ONE FOOT ON THE 'SINGING SWORD', AND HIS FACE TWISTS INTO AN EVIL GRIN.
NEXT WEEK-Arvak!

Prince Valiant
IN THE DAYS OF KING ARTHUR
BY HAROLD R FOSTER

Our Story: WHEN SADOR, WITH UPRAISED SWORD, DASHED TOWARD HIS SPLENDID HORSE, PRINCE VALIANT HURLED THE 'SINGING SWORD' AT HIS LEGS. HE SAVED HIS HORSE, BUT NOW VAL STANDS UNARMED BEFORE HIS GRINNING ENEMY!

WITH SKILLED SHIELD WORK AND NIMBLE FEET, VAL REMAINS ALIVE, LEAPING EVER BACKWARDS. BUT HE IS WATCHING, WATCHING!

HE SEES SADOR LEAN FORWARD, POISED FOR A SUDDEN DASH. VAL DROPS HIS HEAVY SHIELD AND LEAPS IN!

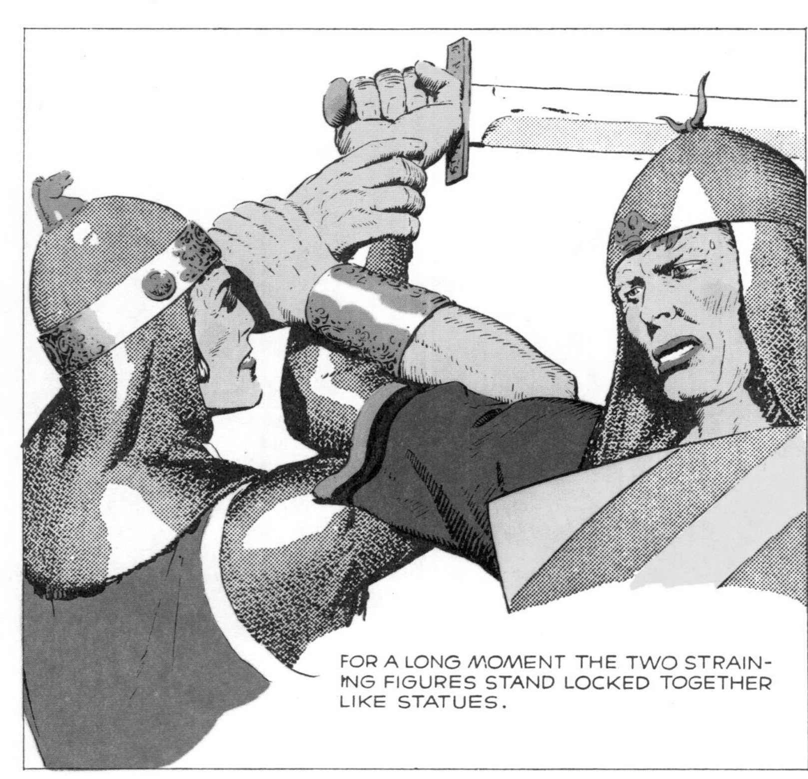

FOR A LONG MOMENT THE TWO STRAINING FIGURES STAND LOCKED TOGETHER LIKE STATUES.

THEN, WITH A BURST OF AWFUL VIOLENCE, VAL THROWS SADOR TO THE TURF WITH A SHATTERED ARM. THE DUEL IS OVER!

"MINE, NOW YOU ARE ALL MINE," WHISPERS VAL. NOT SINCE ALETA PRESENTED HIM WITH THE TWINS HAS HE FELT SUCH PRIDE OF POSSESSION.

HAL FOSTER

ALFRED HAS THOUGHTFULLY BROUGHT ALONG A WINE-SKIN SO VAL CAN CHRISTEN THE RED STALLION IN PROPER FASHION. *"HENCEFORTH YOU WILL BE KNOWN AS 'ARVAK,' AFTER THE CREST I BEAR. 'ARVAK',"* HE EXPLAINS, *"IS THE FIERY HORSE WHO, IN VIKING LEGEND, DRAWS THE SUN'S CHARIOT ACROSS THE SKY."*

NEXT WEEK–Three Men and a Horse.

1074 9-8-57

Prince Valiant
In the Days of King Arthur
By Harold R Foster

Our Story: EACH MORNING PRINCE VALIANT SADDLES ARVAK AND RIDES TO THE PRACTICE FIELD. THERE, BY PATIENT TRAINING, HE WELDS HORSE AND RIDER INTO A PERFECT FIGHTING MACHINE.

THIS LEAVES SQUIRE ALFRED WITH TOO MUCH TIME ON HIS HANDS. HE MEETS SIR GAWAIN'S TWO SERVANTS, PIERRE AND JEX, AND THE THREE AMUSE THEMSELVES TEACHING TRICKS TO...

.....MAYBLOSSOM, A HANDSOME BUT STUPID HORSE OF VAL'S. MAYBLOSSOM IS A NATURAL CLOWN AND CAN BE TAUGHT ANYTHING, PROVIDED IT IS OF NO PRACTICAL VALUE.

SOON, WHAT HAD BEGUN AS IDLE AMUSEMENT TURNS INTO A POLISHED COMEDY ROUTINE. THEY DECIDE TO KEEP THEIR ACT A SECRET...

...FOR A FESTIVAL IS APPROACHING AND THEY PLAN TO AMUSE THE KING AND QUEEN WITH THEIR ABSURD PERFORMANCE.

VAL HAS NO USE FOR MAYBLOSSOM, AND WHEN, IN THE MIDST OF A SCOLDING, THE HORSE PLANTS A WET BUT AFFECTIONATE KISS ON ALFRED'S CHEEK, HE DECIDES TO GET RID OF IT.

TRUMPETS SOUND, AND INTO CAMELOT RIDES HALGAR, THE THUNDERER, ARROGANT CHIEFTAIN OF THE EAST SAXONS.

1075 9-15-57

HAL FOSTER

A LOOK OF ADMIRATION SHINES IN HALGAR'S EYE AS MAYBLOSSOM PRANCES BY. *"MAYBE I CAN UNLOAD HIM ON YON SAXON BOOR!"* MUSES VAL.

NEXT WEEK- **Sold!**

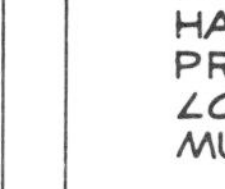

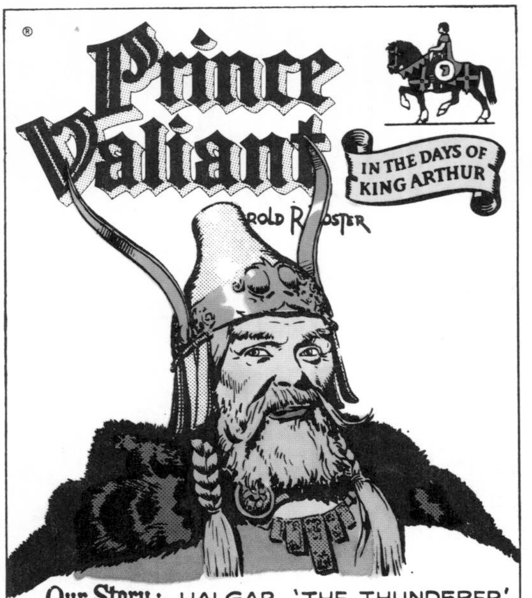
Prince Valiant
IN THE DAYS OF KING ARTHUR
HAROLD R FOSTER
Our Story: HALGAR, 'THE THUNDERER', INSOLENT CHIEFTAIN OF THE EAST SAXONS, RIDES INTO CAMELOT ON A SHAGGY PONY. HIS EYE LIGHTS ON MAYBLOSSOM, ONE OF PRINCE VALIANT'S RIDING HORSES, AND HE LICKS HIS LIPS IN HIS DESIRE TO OWN SUCH A STEED.

VAL SEES THE LOOK ON HIS FACE. "WITH A LITTLE BIT OF LUCK," MUSES VAL, "I MAY BE ABLE TO UNLOAD THAT STUPID COB ON YON BARBARIAN!"

ALAS, NO ONE KNOWS THAT ALFRED, PIERRE AND JEX HAVE SECRETLY TRAINED MAYBLOSSOM TO TAKE PART IN A COMEDY ACT FOR THE COMING FESTIVAL!

WITH BLUSTERING ARROGANCE HALGAR MAKES HIS DEMANDS TO THE KING. AND ARTHUR ANSWERS CALMLY — FOR HALGAR RULES A LARGE DISTRICT — BUT ENDS THE INTERVIEW QUICKLY ...... EVEN A KING'S TEMPER HAS ITS LIMITS.

IT JUST SO HAPPENS THAT WHEN HALGAR RETURNS TO THE COURTYARD, THE HORSE OF HIS DESIRE IS THERE WITH ITS OWNER. WITNESSES SAID AFTERWARD THAT THEY HAD NEVER SEEN SUCH HORSETRADING.......!

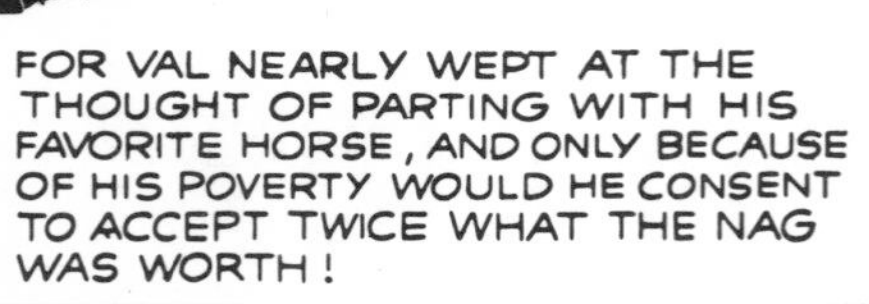
FOR VAL NEARLY WEPT AT THE THOUGHT OF PARTING WITH HIS FAVORITE HORSE, AND ONLY BECAUSE OF HIS POVERTY WOULD HE CONSENT TO ACCEPT TWICE WHAT THE NAG WAS WORTH!

WHEN ALFRED FINDS MAYBLOSSOM MISSING FROM ITS STALL, HE GOES IN SEARCH. HE ARRIVES ON THE SCENE JUST AS HALGAR PREPARES TO MOUNT.
1076. 9-22-57

HAL FOSTER
HE WATCHES IN HORROR. FOR ONLY HE KNOWS THE CAPERS MAYBLOSSOM IS ABOUT TO PERFORM. WAR WITH EAST SAXONY IS IMMINENT!
NEXT WEEK- Circus.
©1957, KING FEATURES SYNDICATE, Inc., WORLD RIGHTS RESERVED.

Prince Valiant
IN THE DAYS OF KING ARTHUR
BY HAROLD R FOSTER

Our Story: HALGAR 'THE THUNDERER' PROUDLY MOUNTS HIS NEWLY PURCHASED HORSE, FEELING THAT AT LAST HE IS MOUNTED AS BEFITS HIS IMPORTANCE. BUT, POOR RIDER THOUGH HE IS, HE HAS NOT GONE MANY YARDS BEFORE HE REALIZES SOMETHING IS AMISS!

AS THOUGH WEARIED BY HIS SPIRITED PRANCING, MAYBLOSSOM LEANS ON THE GATEWAY, CROSSES HIS LEGS AND RESTS.

THE CLAMOR ON HIS BACK MERELY BORES HIM AND HE SITS DOWN AND CLOSES HIS EYES IN PEACEFUL SLUMBER.

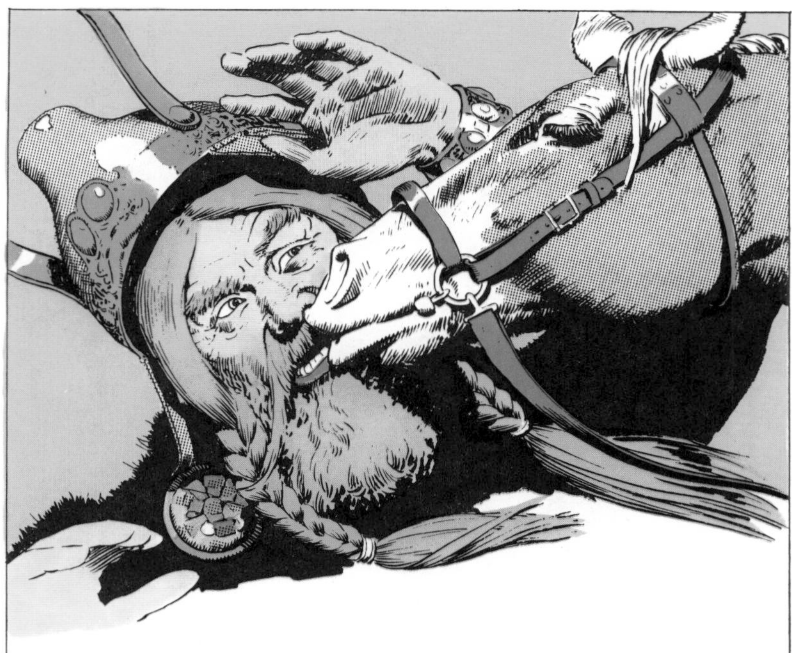

HALGAR DRAWS BACK FROM A WET BUT AFFECTIONATE KISS AND LOSES HIS HELMET.

AS HE STOOPS TO RETRIEVE IT, MAYBLOSSOM GIVES HIM A NUDGE. ROARS OF LAUGHTER FILL MAYBLOSSOM'S HEART WITH JOY... HE HAS GONE THROUGH HIS COMIC ROUTINE AND ACHIEVED SUCCESS!

HALGAR'S FACE IS LIVID WITH RAGE. ONLY BLOOD CAN WIPE OUT THIS INSULT! HE MIGHT EVEN THEN HAVE TAKEN REVENGE HAD HE STAYED, FOR ALL CAMELOT IS WEAK WITH LAUGHTER.

WEAK TOO ARE ALFRED, PIERRE AND JEX, BUT FROM FRIGHT. FOR IT IS THEY WHO, IN SECRET, HAD TAUGHT THE HORSE TO BE A CLOWN.

HAL FOSTER

AND PRINCE VALIANT, WHO SOLD THE HORSE TO HALGAR, WONDERS IF HE HAS NOT STARTED A WAR!

NEXT WEEK-The Whipping.

1077. 9-29-57

®
Prince Valiant
IN THE DAYS OF KING ARTHUR
BY HAROLD R FOSTER

Our Story: ALL CAMELOT ROCKED WITH LAUGHTER WHEN HALGAR, THE SAXON CHIEFTAIN, TRIED TO MOUNT AND RIDE MAYBLOSSOM, A TRICK HORSE. BUT KING ARTHUR IS NOT AMUSED. SUCH AN INCIDENT MIGHT LEAD TO WAR AND BLOODSHED.

ALFRED, PIERRE AND JEX, WHO TRAINED THE HORSE IN SECRET, ARE BROUGHT BEFORE SIR KAY, THE SENESCHAL; AND THEIR PUNISHMENT: A WHIPPING, IN PUBLIC.

PRINCE VALIANT SWEARS AN OATH. ALFRED MUST BE SAVED FROM THE WHIP! FOR THOUGH FATE HAD MADE HIM A SERVANT HE IS OF NOBLE BLOOD AND RIGHTFUL HEIR TO VERNON HALL.

FOR VAL HAD READ THE DRY AND YELLOWED PARCHMENT THAT PROVED HIS NOBLE BIRTH.

AND ALFRED HAD FURTHER PROVED HIS TRUE NOBILITY BY OFFERING THIS PARCHMENT TO LIGHT THE BEACON.....

THE BEACON THAT SHONE OUT ACROSS THE STORMY SEA AND BROUGHT THE LADY HE LOVED SAFELY TO SHORE.....TO BECOME THE BRIDE OF ANOTHER!

SO ALFRED NEVER REACHES THE WHIPPING POST. IT IS A WILD AND RECKLESS DEED THAT MAY WELL SEE VAL OUTLAWED FOR OBSTRUCTING THE KING'S JUSTICE.

IN A NEARBY GROVE THEY FIND THE MOUNTS AND LUGGAGE VAL HAS HIDDEN THERE.

THEN THEY RIDE SWIFTLY TO LONDON TO TAKE PASSAGE ON A SHIP BOUND FOR THULE.
1078 10-6-57

HAL FOSTER
AND THE FIRST FAMILIAR FACE THEY SEE IS AN ANGRY ONE. HALGAR!
NEXT WEEK– The Challenge.
©1957, KING FEATURES SYNDICATE, Inc., WORLD RIGHTS RESERVED

Prince Valiant
IN THE DAYS OF KING ARTHUR
BY HAROLD R FOSTER
Our Story: HALGAR SITS ALONE WITH HIS RAGE. HE HAS BEEN LAUGHED AT! POMPOUS AND ARROGANT, HE CANNOT STAND BEING THE BUTT OF A JOKE. THEN HE LOOKS UP AND SEES PRINCE VALIANT.

PRINCE VALIANT! THE ONE WHO SOLD HIM THE TRICK HORSE THAT MADE HIM LOOK SO RIDICULOUS..

THERE IS NO DOUBT THAT HALGAR IS GOING TO AROUSE THE EAST SAXONS AND SEEK BLOOD VENGEANCE. HIS BLUSTERING WEARS VAL'S TEMPER THIN.

"CLOWN! YOU WERE LAUGHED OUT OF CAMELOT!" HE SHOUTS. "YOUR OWN MEN SAW YOUR COMIC RIDE! YOU WILL BE LAUGHED RIGHT OUT OF BRITAIN! ONLY I HAVE THE SECRET THAT MIGHT SAVE YOU."

HALGAR FEARS THAT THESE WORDS ARE TRUE. "WHAT SECRET?" HE ASKS SULLENLY. VAL CALLS FOR PEN AND PARCHMENT AND WRITES: "I, HALGAR, RODE THE HORSE MAYBLOSSOM WITHOUT WHIP OR SPUR. I CHALLENGE ARTHUR'S KNIGHTS TO DO LIKEWISE, IF THEY DARE!"

"SIGN THIS CHALLENGE AND SEND IT TO CAMELOT WITH THE HORSE MAYBLOSSOM, AND THE LAUGH WILL BE TURNED FROM YOU. OH, HOW I WOULD LIKE TO SEE SIR GAWAIN RIDE HIM!"
A PICTURE TAKES FORM IN HALGAR'S DULL MIND. HE SMILES, AND AFTER VAL HAS ORDERED THE WASSAIL BOWL FILLED AGAIN, EVEN LAUGHS.
1079 10-13-57

HAL FOSTER
HALGAR WILL NOT NOW SEEK VENGEANCE, AND VAL MAY ESCAPE BEING OUTLAWED BY THE KING. A HAPPY EVENT THAT HALGAR CELEBRATES ENTHUSIASTICALLY.
NEXT WEEK-Homing.

Prince Valiant
IN THE DAYS OF KING ARTHUR
BY HAROLD R FOSTER

Our Story: IN THE TWISTING, CLUTTERED STREETS OF LONDON PRINCE VALIANT GOES SHOPPING... GIFTS FOR THE FOLKS AT HOME AND AN OUTFIT FOR ALFRED MORE IN KEEPING WITH HIS POSITION.

THEN COMES THE SEARCH FOR A VESSEL TO CARRY THEM ACROSS THE NORTH SEA, AND WHEN THEY FINALLY FIND ONE, THE ENDLESS HAGGLING OVER THE FARE.

NO STEED EVER RECEIVED MORE CARE THAN ARVAK; PERHAPS BECAUSE NO ONE WAS EVER MORE FOND OR PROUD OF HIS HORSE THAN VAL.

AND WHEN THE NIGHT IS WILD WITH WIND AND THE SPRAY STINGS LIKE A WHIPLASH, VAL STANDS BY ARVAK TO CALM HIS FEARS.

HAL FOSTER

THULE AT LAST AND THEY COME IN FROM THE ROLLING SEA TO THE SHELTER OF HUGE ISLANDS, AND SAIL NORTHWARD PAST THE AWFUL GRANDEUR OF A COAST THAT KNOWS NO EQUAL.

NEXT WEEK- The Calm One.

1080 10-20-57

Prince Valiant
IN THE DAYS OF KING ARTHUR
BY HAROLD R FOSTER

Our Story: IT IS ONLY A SHORT SAIL UP THE FJORD TO VIKINGSHOLM, BUT ARVAK IS DROOPING FROM WANT OF EXERCISE. PRINCE VALIANT ORDERS THE VESSEL TO LAND AT TRONDHEIM.

HE SENDS A RUNNER OFF TO THE CASTLE WITH A MESSAGE ANNOUNCING HIS ARRIVAL A FEW DAYS HENCE.

ALETA RECEIVES THE MESSAGE QUIETLY AND FOR A LONG MOMENT PRESSES IT AGAINST HER HEART. THEN SHE BREAKS THE NEWS.

"PRINCE VALIANT IS COMING! PUT UP THE TAPESTRIES! SCRUB THE FLOORS! POLISH THE SILVER! OPEN THE WINE CELLAR! PRINCE VALIANT IS COMING! PRINCE VAL..........!!!"

"PRINCE VALIANT IS COMING, KATWIN! I'LL WEAR THE CRIMSON GOWN WITH THE GOLD GIRDLE! NO, THE PURPLE AND SILVER. OH, DEAR, I HAVEN'T A THING TO WEAR!"

"AND WE MUST DO MY HAIR A NEW WAY! NOW, DON'T GET EXCITED, KATWIN! BE CALM!"
BUT ALETA CANNOT SIT STILL AND EVEN KATWIN'S PATIENCE REACHES AN END. IN ALL THE WORLD ONLY KATWIN IS PRIVILEGED TO BULLY THIS SMALL QUEEN.....

"ENOUGH OF THIS! HE WILL NOT ARRIVE UNTIL THE MORROW AND HE WILL NOT NOTICE WHETHER YOU ARE WEARING SILK OR SACK-CLOTH. AND YOUR HAIR WILL BE MUSSED UP ONE MOMENT AFTER HE ARRIVES!"

HAL FOSTER
DAY ENDS AND VAL RIDES ON IN THE MOONLIGHT. HE MAY NOT SLEEP THIS NIGHT, BUT HE WILL DREAM.
NEXT WEEK- The Water Maiden.
1081 10-27-57

Prince Valiant
IN THE DAYS OF KING ARTHUR
BY HAROLD R FOSTER

Our Story: ALETA DOES NOT SLEEP MUCH THAT NIGHT. AT EVERY SOUND FROM THE COURTYARD SHE RUSHES TO THE WINDOW TO SEE IF IT MIGHT BE THE ARRIVAL OF PRINCE VALIANT. AT DAWN SHE CALLS KATWIN TO HELP HER DRESS. BUT FOR THIS DAY OF DAYS NO GOWN IS PRETTY ENOUGH.

AT LAST A WEARY KATWIN SAYS: "PRINCE VALIANT ALWAYS ADMIRED YOU ON A HORSE. AND IF YOU DO RIDE OUT YOU WILL MEET HIM THE SOONER!"

AN HOUR LATER SHE SEES HER LORD AND VICTIM COMING DOWN THE TRAIL. WITH WILDLY BEATING HEART SHE GALLOPS DOWN TO THE FORD TO MEET HIM.

ALAS FOR THE HOURS SPENT ON HAIRDRESSING, COSTUME, PERFUME AND POWDER. HER MOUNT STUMBLES!

BUT SHE HAS LOST NONE OF HER MAGIC. THE MAGIC THAT MAKES VAL'S HEART DO STRANGE TRICKS. THERE IS A LUMP IN HIS THROAT AND HIS VOICE TREMBLES. HE PRETENDS NOT TO RECOGNIZE HER.

"AH, WASHING YOUR CLOTHES, I SEE!" HE EXCLAIMS, "AND RATHER PRETTY FOR A WASHERWOMAN, TOO. MAY I GIVE YOU A LIFT?"

"I AM SURE MY WIFE WILL NOT MIND IF I CHARGE YOU A KISS FOR THE RIDE."
1082
11-3-57

HAL FOSTER
NOW TURN THE PAGE GENTLY, READER, FOR THIS MOMENT IS SACRED TO THESE TWO.
NEXT WEEK- The Rut.

Prince Valiant
IN THE DAYS OF KING ARTHUR
BY HAROLD R. FOSTER

Our Story: SO PRINCE VALIANT PICKED HIS WIFE OUT OF THE RIVER AND THEY RODE HOME TOGETHER. AND IT WAS JUST AS KATWIN SAID; HE NEVER NOTICED HOW HER HAIR WAS FIXED OR WHAT SHE WORE.

"WHO IS THIS?" DEMANDS KATWIN. *"IT DOES NOT LOOK MUCH LIKE THE MISTRESS I SPENT HOURS TO DRESS, COMB, BRUSH, POWDER, PERFUME AND BEJEWEL!"*

BUT ALETA ONLY SMILES UP AT HER HANDSOME LORD AND MASTER. FOR, BY THE RATHER STUPID, ADORING LOOK ON HIS FACE, SHE KNOWS HE IS STILL COMPLETELY HERS.

NEXT TO GREET VAL ARE THE TWINS. HE IS ALMOST A STRANGER TO THEM. AND KAREN GAZES AT HIM BOLDLY; SHE WILL DEMAND HER RIGHTFUL PLACE IN HIS AFFECTIONS. VALETA SMILES PRETTILY AND FLUTTERS HER LASHES; SHE PLANS TO WIND HIM AROUND HER LITTLE FINGER.

ARN ARRIVES, BREATHLESS, FOLLOWED BY THE EVER-PRESENT SIR GAWAIN. HE HAS GROWN IN THE PAST MONTHS, TALL AND STURDY, AND VAL IS GRATEFUL THAT GOD HAS GRANTED HIM SUCH A SON.

HAL FOSTER

KING AGUAR IS HAPPY TO HAVE HIS STALWART SON ONCE MORE AT HIS SIDE TO SHARE THE BURDEN OF STATECRAFT. AND SAD ALSO, FOR DURING VAL'S ABSENCE HE HAS SPENT THIS SUNSET HOUR IN THE NURSERY WITH ALETA AND HIS GRANDCHILDREN. NOW HE PLAYS SECOND FIDDLE TO HIS OWN SON. FRANKLY, HE IS A BIT JEALOUS!

NEXT WEEK- **A Time of Parting.**

1083 11-10-57

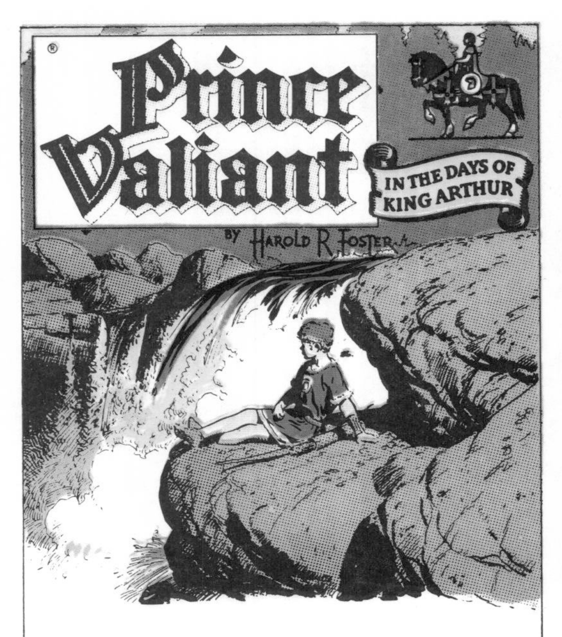

Prince Valiant
IN THE DAYS OF KING ARTHUR
BY HAROLD R. FOSTER

Our Story: ON HIS FAVORITE PERCH PRINCE ARN SITS DREAMING OF THE DAY WHEN HE CAN GO ADVENTURING AND SEE STRANGE PLACES. HE CANNOT GUESS THAT THE DAY IS AT HAND.

HIGH ON THE PASS TO THE INNER LANDS, WHERE WINTER'S SNOWS STILL LINGER, A HORSEMAN PICKS HIS DANGEROUS WAY.

AT DAY'S END HE ENTERS VIKINGSHOLM AND ASKS TO SEE PRINCE VALIANT.

"HAP-ATLA, KING OF THE INNER LANDS, IS SENDING HIS SON HERE. IN RETURN ARN IS TO BE FOSTER SON TO HAP-ATLA. SO WE AGREED LONG AGO."

VAL WISHES TO SPEND THESE LAST DAYS WITH HIS SON, HAWKING OR FISHING, BUT ARN IS TOO EXCITED. HE PACKS AND UNPACKS A DOZEN TIMES. VAL FOLLOWS HIM AROUND DEJECTEDLY, WISHING HE HAD BEEN MORE OF A COMPANION.

WHEN AT LAST EVERYTHING IS PACKED, ARN GOES TO THE MEWS AND TAKES HIS FALCON FROM HER PERCH. THIS HAWK HE HAD CAPTURED AND TRAINED FOR HUNTING ALL BY HIMSELF.

IN THE FIELD HE REMOVES HOOD, LEASH AND JESSES AND GIVES HER THE FREEDOM SHE HAS EARNED.

1084 11-17-57

HAL FOSTER

IT IS ONLY WHEN HE SITS WITH HIS DOG, SIR GAWAIN, ABSORBING THE LOVE AND DEVOTION THAT ONLY A DOG CAN GIVE, THAT HE REALIZES THAT HE MUST LEAVE BEHIND ALL HE LOVES AND ALL WHO LOVE HIM.

NEXT WEEK-**Brave Good-bye.**

Prince Valiant
IN THE DAYS OF KING ARTHUR
BY HAROLD R FOSTER
Our Story: AT DAWN THE PONIES STAND READY AND WAITING TO TAKE PRINCE ARN ACROSS THE MOUNTAINS TO THE INNER LANDS AND HIS FOSTER HOME......

....WHILE ARN SAYS GOOD-BYE TO HIS MOTHER IN PRIVATE. FOR NO ONE SHOULD SEE TEARS IN THE EYES OF A MANLY YOUNG PRINCE.

A CASUAL HANDSHAKE FOR HIS FATHER AND THE KING, THEN HE LEAPS TO HIS SADDLE AND LEADS HIS LITTLE TROOP AWAY, HIS BACK STRAIGHT AND HEAD HELD HIGH.

BUT ARN IS VERY YOUNG AND SOON EXCHANGES THE SORROW OF PARTING FOR THE EXCITEMENT OF NEW ADVENTURES AHEAD.

THEY CROSS THE PASS AND LOOK DOWN ON THE VAST FORESTS OF THE INNER LANDS, AND FAR BELOW SUN-LIGHT FLASHES ON STEEL, AND ARN'S GUIDES LOOSEN THE SWORDS IN THEIR SCABBARDS.

THE TWO BANDS APPROACH EACH OTHER WARILY, AND AFTER MUCH SHOUTING BACK AND FORTH, THEY MEET.

HAL FOSTER
"I AM SVEN, SON OF HAP-ATLA, KING OF THE INNER LANDS, ON MY WAY TO SERVE PRINCE VALIANT."
"AND I AM ARN, SON OF PRINCE VALIANT. THEN WE ARE FOSTER BROTHERS! LET US DISMOUNT AND CAMP HERE FOR THE NIGHT."
NEXT WEEK - In Confidence.
1085

Prince Valiant
IN THE DAYS OF KING ARTHUR
BY HAROLD R FOSTER

Our Story: IN ACCORDANCE WITH AGE-OLD CUSTOM, PRINCE VALIANT AND KING HAP-ATLA EXCHANGE SONS. ON THEIR WAY TO THEIR NEW HOMES THE TWO FOSTER BROTHERS MEET AND LIKE EACH OTHER AT ONCE.

"MY FATHER, PRINCE VALIANT, IS A GREAT WARRIOR AND COMMANDS ARMIES WITH EASE, BUT IF YOU GET MOTHER ON YOUR SIDE, YOU HAVE NOTHING TO FEAR!"

"WHY, IT IS THE SAME AT OUR HOME! MOTHER IS SOFT AND GENTLE, BUT SHE CAN WIND THE KING AROUND HER LITTLE FINGER. BUT BEWARE OF MY SISTER – SHE IS A MONSTER!"

"I HAVE TWIN SISTERS WHO WILL PLAGUE YOU WITHOUT END. MOTHER WILL BE OF NO HELP TO YOU THERE – SHE THINKS THEY ARE CUTE! MY FATHER DOES NOT UNDERSTAND CHILDREN OR WOMEN, AND THE KING IS NOT AS STERN AS HE LOOKS. MAKE UP TO GARM, THE HUNTER. HE'S FUN!"

BY THE TIME THE FOSTER BROTHERS PART, THERE IS LITTLE THEY DON'T KNOW ABOUT THEIR NEW HOMES AND THE FOLKS THEREIN. THEN THEY EXCHANGE GIFTS. ARN PARTS WITH HIS FAVORITE BOW, AND SVEN GIVES HIM HIS SAXEKNIFE AND BELT IN RETURN.

AND SVEN ARRIVES AT VIKINGSHOLM WITH SOME MISGIVINGS. THE TWINS ARE REGARDING HIM WITH GRINS OF DEVILISH GLEE, LIKE TWO SMALL HARPIES WITH A FRESH VICTIM

HAL FOSTER

WHILE ARN IS MEETING HIS FOSTER PARENTS HE SEES THE 'MONSTER', AND SHE IS NOT HIDEOUS AS REPORTED. IN FACT, SHE LOOKS RATHER NICE.

NEXT WEEK – THE "Monster."

1086 12 1-57

Prince Valiant
IN THE DAYS OF KING ARTHUR
BY HAROLD R FOSTER

Our Story: PRINCE ARN ARRIVES AT HIS NEW HOME AND IS GREETED BY HIS FOSTER PARENTS. HE ALSO MEETS FRYTHA, A SWEET CHILD WHO LOOKS NOTHING LIKE THE 'MONSTER' SHE IS REPORTED TO BE.

THEN HE CALLS TO HIS MEN TO BRING IN THE RICH GIFTS HIS FATHER HAS SENT HAP-ATLA AND HIS QUEEN. FINALLY THE CHESTS ARE EMPTY, BUT NO GIFT IS THERE FOR FRYTHA.

"FOR YOU," SAYS ARN GALLANTLY AND HANDS HER HIS MOST CHERISHED POSSESSION, HIS BELT AND SAXEKNIFE. TEARS OF GRATITUDE FILL HER PRETTY EYES AT THIS GENEROUS GESTURE. SHE RUNS FROM THE HALL.....

.....STRAIGHT TO ARN'S ROOM WHERE SHE REMOVES THE SNAKE SHE HAD PUT IN HIS BED AND THE BURS FROM HIS PILLOW......

AND BACK IN HER OWN ROOM, SHE SADLY DISCARDS THE RIPE FISH SHE MEANT TO PLACE IN HIS CLOTHES CHEST, THE TACKS FOR HIS CHAIR AND THE GLUE TO FILL HIS SHOES. HER DAY IS SPOILED!

THE LEOPARD CANNOT CHANGE ITS SPOTS, NOR CAN FRYTHA BECOME AN ANGEL ALL AT ONCE. *"WOULD YOU LIKE TO SEE THE GREAT PIKE IN THE FISH POND?"*

1087 12-8-57

HAL FOSTER

AND SHE SHOVES HIM IN!

NEXT WEEK - **Tit for Tat.**

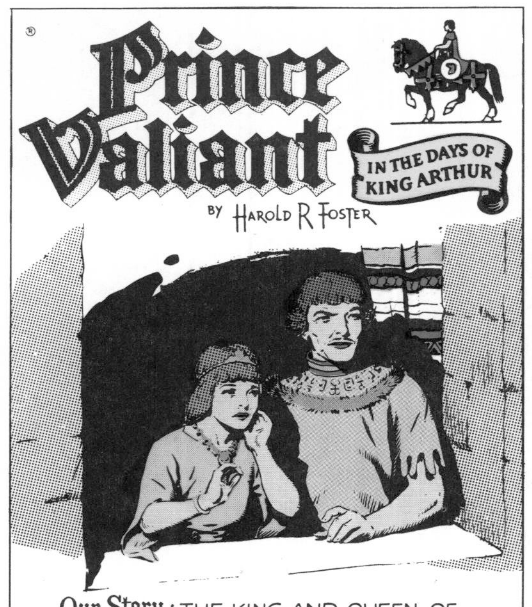
Prince Valiant
IN THE DAYS OF KING ARTHUR
BY HAROLD R. FOSTER

Our Story: THE KING AND QUEEN OF THE INNER LANDS WATCH FROM A WINDOW AS THEIR PRETTY LITTLE GIRL (KNOWN AS THE 'MONSTER') PUSHES HER FOSTER BROTHER INTO THE FISH POND. THEY ARE QUITE USED TO THINGS LIKE THIS.

PRINCE ARN AND A LOT OF MUD COME UP OUT OF THE POND. HE IS NOT ONE-HALF AS HAPPY AS FRYTHA.

LONG AGO ARN LEARNED HOW THIS IS DONE FROM ASSOCIATING WITH HIS MOTHER. HE DOES A FAIR JOB.

"HOW DARE YOU STRIKE A PRINCESS, YOU HORRID BEAST? I'LL HAVE YOU WHIPPED! I'LL CUT YOUR HEART OUT! I'LL"..... AND SHE SLAPS HIM.

ARN EVENS THE SCORE NEATLY.

THE KING GRABS HIS WIFE JUST IN TIME AND DRAWS HER BACK FROM THE WINDOW. *"QUIET,"* HE WHISPERS.

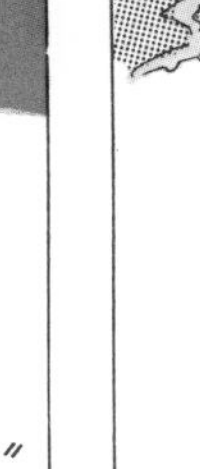

"ARE YOU GOING TO LET THAT LITTLE BULLY ABUSE YOUR DAUGHTER?" BUT THE KING ONLY SMILES WISTFULLY: *"WOULD IT NOT BE LOVELY IF AT LAST SHE HAS MET HER MATCH?"*

1088 12-15-57

HAL FOSTER

"WHAT A MAN!" MURMURS THE 'MONSTER' ADMIRINGLY. *"EVEN SO, BOILING IN OIL IS TOO GOOD FOR HIM!"*

NEXT WEEK–**Lonely People.**

Prince Valiant
IN THE DAYS OF KING ARTHUR
BY HAROLD R FOSTER
Our Story: IT IS AN AGE-OLD CUSTOM FOR THE NOBILITY TO EXCHANGE SONS FOR TRAINING. BUT PRINCE VALIANT IS WORRIED. IS ARN WELL? IS HE BEING PROPERLY CARED FOR? IS HE, PERHAPS, HOMESICK?
THEN HE SEES A LONELY LITTLE BOY WANDERING SADLY IN THE COURTYARD ...SVEN, HIS FOSTER SON!

"ARE YOU HOMESICK, SVEN?", VAL ASKS. "OH, NO, SIR", LIES SVEN BRAVELY, "BUT THIS LAND IS SO BIG, SO ROUGH, SO UNLIKE HOME!"

BUT AN HOUR LATER WHEN HE HAS SPEARED AND LANDED HIS FIRST SALMON, IT WOULD SEEM THAT THIS LAND IS NOT SO BAD, AFTER ALL!

ARN'S DAYS ARE BUSY. HE SERVES AS PAGE BOY WHEN KING HAP-ATLA HOLDS COURT, STUDIES IN THE CLASSROOM, PRACTICES IN THE ARMORY, BUT ALL THE WHILE HIS HEART IS IN THE WINDY FJORDS AND RUGGED MOUNTAINS OF VIKINGSHOLM.

HUMANS MAY HIDE THEIR FEELINGS, BUT NOT SIR GAWAIN. NIGHT AND DAY HE TELLS THE WORLD OF HIS LONGING FOR HIS MASTER. HE REFUSES TO EAT.

"I AM WORRIED, LADY QUEEN," SAYS GARM THE HUNTER. "THE YOUNG MASTER CHARGED ME TO CARE FOR HIS DOG, BUT HE WILL GRIEVE HIMSELF TO DEATH ERE LONG."
1089 12-22-57

HAL FOSTER
NEXT DAWN GARM TAKES THE LONG, HARD ROAD TO THE INNER LANDS, THAT A BOY AND HIS DOG MAY BE TOGETHER AGAIN.
NEXT WEEK:
Sir Gawain's Supreme Test.

Prince Valiant
In the days of King Arthur
By Harold R Foster

Our Story: TO SAVE SIR GAWAIN FROM GRIEVING TO DEATH, GARM THE HUNTER MAKES THE LONG JOURNEY TO THE INNER LANDS TO TAKE HIM TO HIS MASTER.

"YOU ARE THE MOST STUPID, USELESS DOG IN ALL THE WORLD, BUT IF YOU CAN MAKE MASTER ARN ANY HAPPIER, THIS TRIP IS WORTH WHILE!"

WHEN HIS DAY'S DUTIES ARE OVER, PRINCE ARN WANDERS AFIELD, LONELY AND HOMESICK IN THIS ALIEN LAND.

HE TRESPASSES ON A BERRY PATCH OCCUPIED BY A BEAR. USUALLY A BEAR WILL LUMBER OFF, BUT THIS ONE IS PROTECTING ITS CUB. IN THE DISTANCE ARN HEARS A HOUND GIVE VOICE.

ARN'S LIGHT BOW COULD NOT STOP ITS CHARGE, BUT AS THE BAYING OF THE HOUND GROWS LOUDER THE BEAR HESITATES...

...AND OUT OF THE WOODS GALLOPS SIR GAWAIN, QUIVERING WITH FEAR BUT WILLING TO FACE ANY DANGER THAT THREATENS HIS BELOVED MASTER. THEN GARM RUNS UP, SHOUTING, AND THE BEAR RETREATS.

1090. 12-29-57

HAL FOSTER

ONLY A FLEA-RIDDEN MONGREL, BUT HE HAS THE POWER TO BANISH A BOY'S LONELINESS WITH HIS UNSTINTING LOVE.

NEXT WEEK–
The Council of Kings.

Prince Valiant
IN THE DAYS OF KING ARTHUR
BY HAROLD R FOSTER

Our Story: FOR THE FIRST TIME SINCE COMING TO THIS ALIEN LAND PRINCE ARN GOES TO SLEEP WITH A CONTENTED SMILE ON HIS FACE. THE ARRIVAL OF HIS DOG HAS BANISHED ALL LONELINESS. HIS FOSTER PARENTS ARE GLAD TO SEE HIM HAPPY AGAIN, IN SPITE OF THE MUDDY PAW MARKS, DOG HAIR AND FLEAS.

ON THE EVE OF THE 'COUNCIL OF KINGS' KING AGUAR IS THROWN FROM HIS HORSE AND INJURED.

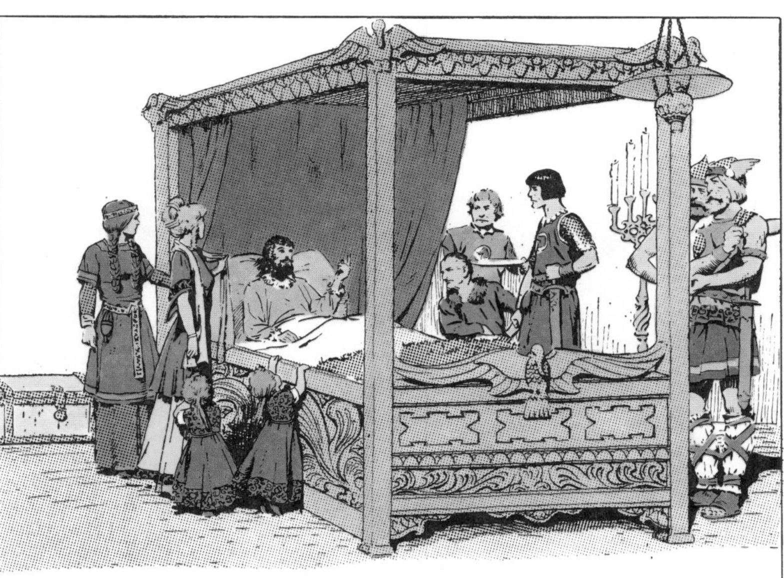

"YOU WILL HAVE TO GO IN MY STEAD, VAL. AND YOU WILL HAVE TO FACE THE ENMITY OF THOSE WHO WISH US TO JOIN THEM IN WAR ON THE DANES. WITHOUT THE AID OF THULE THEY DARE NOT ATTEMPT IT. BEWARE OF TREACHERY!"

VAL SAILS WITH TWELVE GOOD SHIPS. FOR THOUGH ALL WEAPONS AND VIOLENCE ARE BARRED FROM THE COUNCIL, ANYTHING CAN HAPPEN ON THE WAY BACK.

HE LANDS AT BERGEN, THE MEETING PLACE, IN ONLY ONE SHIP, AND CERTAIN CHIEFTAINS ARE DISAPPOINTED. THEY HAVE LAID PLANS TO TRAP AN EAGLE, NOT A GAMECOCK.

HAL FOSTER

EVERY FIVE YEARS THE 'COUNCIL OF KINGS' MEETS TO ADJUST BOUNDARIES, MAKE ALLIANCES OR RENEW OLD HATREDS, AND AGUAR, 'THE EAGLE OF THULE,' HAS ALWAYS DOMINATED THE MEETINGS. WHILE THEY ADMITTED THE WISDOM OF HIS DECISIONS, THEIR FIERCE HEARTS DEMANDED THE VIOLENCE OF RAIDS, PLUNDERING AND WAR.

NEXT WEEK - **The Sea Fight.**

1091 1-5-58

Prince Valiant
IN THE DAYS OF KING ARTHUR
BY HAROLD R FOSTER

Our Story: KING HAP-ATLA OF THE 'INNER LANDS' COMES TO THE COUNCIL BRINGING ARN WITH HIM, AND FATHER AND SON HAVE A HAPPY REUNION.
"BUT WHY DID YOU NOT BRING MY SON WITH YOU, VALIANT?"

"BECAUSE THE GROWING ENMITY AGAINST THULE MAY BREAK OUT IN VIOLENCE AND MAKE THE JOURNEY HOME A DANGEROUS ONE. YOUR SON SVEN IS TOO YOUNG FOR WAR."

AS THE COUNCIL OF KINGS COMES TO A CLOSE, PRINCE VALIANT STANDS ALONE IN HIS DECISION TO AVOID A RUINOUS WAR. AND MANY SAY KING AGUAR IS TOO OLD AND FEEBLE FOR THE JOYS OF FIGHTING AND HIS SON IS TOO TIMID!

AS THE COUNCILORS DEPART THE CAPTAIN OF VAL'S SHIP REPORTS: "YOUR SHIPS ARE HIDDEN IN THE NEXT FJORD, BUT OUTSIDE MANY LONGSHIPS ARE GATHERING."

DODGING AMONG THE ISLANDS, RISKING THE SHOALS, VAL JOINS HIS FLEET. BUT BEHIND HIM COME ARMED FIGHTING SHIPS BENT ON DESTROYING THE POWER OF THULE.

VAL HAS BUT A SHORT TIME TO SHOUT THE PLAN OF BATTLE TO HIS CAPTAINS BEFORE THE SHIPS CRASH FURIOUSLY TOGETHER.

HAL FOSTER
IT SEEMS AS IF PRINCE VALIANT REALLY IS TIMID, FOR HE ORDERS THE RETREAT OF HIS LITTLE FLEET. IN CLOSE ORDER THEY FLEE UP THE FJORD TO CERTAIN CAPTURE. VAL WATCHES THE WILD PURSUIT AND THE FOG THAT IS ROLLING IN FROM THE SEA.
NEXT WEEK-
Battle in the Fog.

Prince Valiant
IN THE DAYS OF KING ARTHUR
BY HAROLD R FOSTER
Our Story: WITH FIERCE SHOUTS OF TRIUMPH THE PURSUERS STRAIN AT THEIR OARS, EAGER TO BE THE FIRST TO SLASH INTO PRINCE VALIANT'S RETREATING FLEET. VAL WATCHES HIS ENEMIES AS THEY STRING OUT BEHIND THE CLOSE RANKS OF HIS SHIPS. HE ALSO WATCHES THE FOG OBSCURE ONE AFTER ANOTHER OF THE PURSUERS.

A HORN BLARES ITS MESSAGE AND VAL'S FLEET TURNS AND GOES BACK ON ITS COURSE, ITS CLOSE RANKS MEETING THE PURSUERS SINGLY ONE AFTER ANOTHER. THE ENEMY HAVE BEEN DECOYED BY THE OLDEST TRICK IN WARFARE!

THEIR WAKE IS LITTERED WITH THE WRECKAGE OF MANY ONCE-PROUD SHIPS, SOME OF THEM VAL'S. TOO FEW NOW TO MEET THE MAIN BODY OF THE ENEMY, VAL SOUNDS THE SIGNAL FOR THE NEXT MANEUVER.

HIS REMAINING VESSELS TURN RIGHT AND LEFT TO THE VERY SHORES OF THE FJORD, LEAVING THE ENEMY TO SAIL UP THE MIDDLE IN THE FOG TO THE VERY END AND FIND.... NOTHING!

THE REMNANT OF VAL'S FLEET FEELS ITS WAY TO A RENDEZVOUS FAR OUT AT SEA...ALL BUT ONE. VAL'S SHIP, VEERING AWAY FROM A JAGGED ROCK, RUNS INTO A SUBMERGED ONE.

1093 1·19·58

HAL FOSTER
ALL AROUND THEM THEY CAN HEAR THE SOUND OF THE ENEMY, AS THEY STRUGGLE TO FREE THEIR SHIP AND STEM THE LEAK!
NEXT WEEK–The Wanderer.

Prince Valiant
In the Days of King Arthur
By Harold R Foster

Our Story: THEY CAN HEAR THE SOUNDS OF THE ENEMY FLEET SEARCHING FOR THEM IN THE FOG, WHILE THEIR OWN SHIP IS HELD FIRMLY ON THE SHOAL. STRIPPING OFF HIS ARMOR, PRINCE VALIANT TIES A LONG CORD TO HIS WAIST AND DIVES OVERBOARD.

HE SWIMS TO A NEARBY ROCK AND PULLS OVER A STOUT ROPE, AND HIS WARRIORS HEAVE THE VESSEL INTO DEEPER WATER.

BEFORE THEY CAN STEM THE LEAK IN THE SHATTERED BOW, AN ENEMY SHIP LOOMS UP THROUGH THE MIST AND A WILD FIGHT ENSUES.

THE FOG IS LIFTING, AND VAL CAN SEE THAT HIS OWN BOAT IS SINKING. TO BE DISCOVERED NOW WILL MEAN DEATH. HE STRIKES OUT FOR SHORE.

HIS SHIP IS AWASH, DRIFTING, EMPTY. THE OTHER IS SPEEDING TOWARD HIM, THE WARRIORS SHOUTING IN TRIUMPH, WAVING THEIR WEAPONS.

VAL ESCAPES UP THE CLIFF. HOW IS HE TO KNOW THAT THEY ARE HIS OWN MEN WHO HAVE CONQUERED THE ENEMY AND ARE COMING TO HIS RESCUE?

IN THE FJORD BEHIND HIM VAL SEES THE REMNANT OF THE ENEMY FLEET STILL SEARCHING FOR HIS TWELVE SHIPS. ONLY A VAST AMOUNT OF WRECKAGE GIVES PROOF THAT ONCE THEY REALLY WERE THERE.

HAL FOSTER

1094. 1-26-58

NEXT WEEK- **Pursuit.**

Prince Valiant
IN THE DAYS OF KING ARTHUR
BY HAROLD R FOSTER

Our Story: PRINCE VALIANT'S SMALL FLEET AVOIDS A TRAP AND ESCAPES SAFELY TO SEA LEAVING BEHIND A VAST AMOUNT OF WRECKAGE. VAL IS PART OF THAT ABANDONED WRECKAGE.

AS HE BATHES THE WOUNDS THAT ARE SO MUCH A PART OF HIS VOCATION, VAL WATCHES THE ENEMY SHIPS SALVAGE WHAT THEY CAN OF THEIR LOSSES. HE HOPES THEY WILL OVERLOOK SOMETHING, FOR HE IS UNARMED AND PRACTICALLY NAKED.

IN A PEACEFUL COVE SOME OF THE GRIM FRUITS OF WAR COME ASHORE. AN UNPLEASANT TASK, BUT VAL IS DESPERATE FOR WEAPONS AND CLOTHES.

THREE HUNDRED MILES OF MOUNTAIN, RIVER, FOREST AND FJORD LIE BETWEEN HIM AND VIKINGSHOLM. IN A HIGH MEADOW HE FINDS A LONELY OUTFARM AND IS GIVEN FOOD AND SHELTER.

HE IS UP AND AWAY AT DAWN, FOR HE IS IN ENEMY COUNTRY, AND SOON THESE GOOD PEOPLE WILL LEARN OF THE BATTLE AT THE FJORD.

AT A TURN IN THE VALLEY HE LOOKS BACK. SUNLIGHT FLASHES ON STEEL! ARMED MEN ARE SEARCHING FOR STRAGGLERS FROM THE BATTLE. SHOULD THEY LEARN HIS IDENTITY, THERE REALLY WILL BE A CHASE!

HAL FOSTER
AHEAD LOOMS THE FIRST OBSTACLE ON HIS HOMEWARD JOURNEY, THE GREAT JOSTEDAL GLACIER!
NEXT WEEK- Sun, Ice and Wind!
1095.
2-2-58

Prince Valiant
IN THE DAYS OF KING ARTHUR
BY HAROLD R. FOSTER
Our Story: HIGH ABOVE, THE JOSTEDAL GLACIER GLEAMS IN THE MORNING SUNLIGHT; BELOW, HIS PURSUERS CLIMB SWIFTLY, CLIMB AS IF THEY HAVE GUESSED HE IS PRINCE VALIANT, AND WORTH A RICH REWARD.

THE GLACIER OFFERS NO ESCAPE; A HUNDRED YAWNING CREVASSES WAIT TO TRAP ANYONE WHO VENTURES UPON ITS CRUMBLING EDGE.

IF ONLY THE 'SINGING SWORD' WERE AT HAND, HE WOULD TURN AND FACE HIS ENEMIES. VAL ENTERS A HUGE CREVASSE. HERE HE CAN MEET HIS OPPONENTS ONE AT A TIME.

ON AND ON HE GOES INTO THE DRIPPING HEART OF THE MIGHTY GLACIER UNTIL FINALLY IT BECOMES SO NARROW HE CAN INCH HIS WAY UPWARD.
THE TOP AT LAST! BUT HOW TO GET OUT? HE MUST TRUST HIS FULL WEIGHT ON THE SLENDER SHAFT OF HIS SPEAR.

HE HAS GAINED THE SOLID ICE CAP, MILE AFTER MILE OF GLITTERING ICE. THE GLARE IS UNBEARABLE AND THE STABBING PAIN IN HIS EYES FILLS HIM WITH DREAD.

SNOW-BLIND! VAL COVERS HIS HEAD AND SITS DOWN TO AWAIT THE SUN-SET, WONDERING IF HE WILL BE ABLE TO SEE HIS WAY THROUGH THE CRE-VASSES AT THE FAR SIDE.

THE WIND BLOWS UNHINDERED ACROSS THE ICY WASTE, AND WHEN IT GROWS CHILL HE KNOWS THE SUN HAS SET. LIFTING HIS CLOAK HE PEERS AROUND.
1096
2-9-58

HAL FOSTER
A GREEN TWIG! A GREEN TWIG ON THE VERY TOP OF A GLACIER! WHAT CAN IT MEAN?
NEXT WEEK- The Markers.